All Things Law Of Attract

MW00633046

(journals, workbooks, greeting cards, stickers, coffee mugs and more)

Law of Attraction Workbooks are influenced by
Abraham Hicks
https://www.abraham-hicks.com

Identify. Isolate. Calibrate.

Identify

Isolate

Calibrate

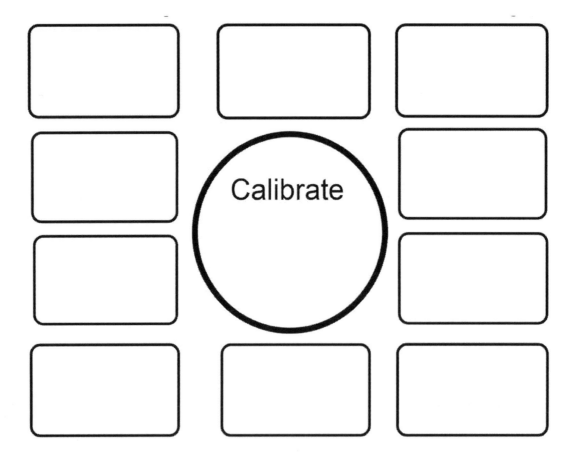

Get out ahead of it. Calibrate!

What is your point of attraction? Point in the direction of what you want.
Observe what your Inner Being knows. Tell it the way you want it.

_____

_____

_____

_____

_____

_____

_____

_____

_____

_____

_____

_____

_____

_____

_____

_____

_____

_____

_____

_____

_____

_____

_____

Identify. Isolate. Calibrate.

Identify

Isolate

Calibrate

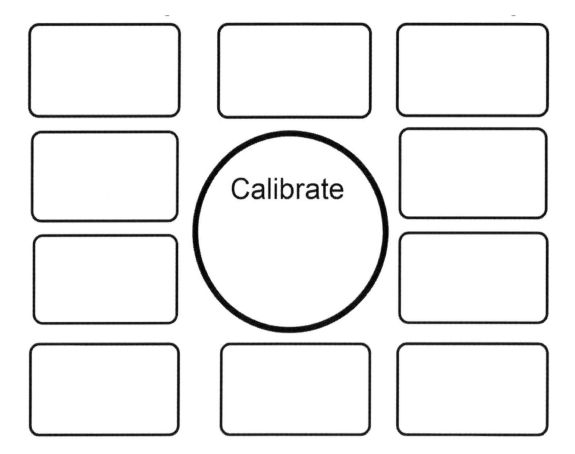

Get out ahead of it. Calibrate!

What is your point of attraction? Point in the direction of what you want.
Observe what your Inner Being knows. Tell it the way you want it.

_____

_____

_____

_____

_____

_____

_____

_____

_____

_____

_____

_____

_____

_____

_____

_____

_____

_____

_____

_____

_____

_____

_____

_____

Identify. Isolate. Calibrate.

Identify

Isolate

Calibrate

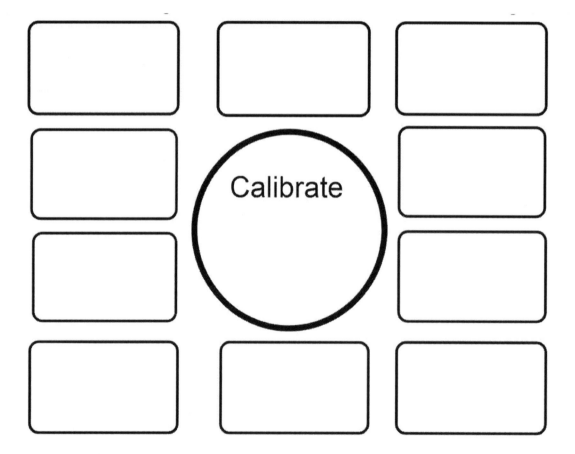
Calibrate

Get out ahead of it. Calibrate!

What is your point of attraction? Point in the direction of what you want.
Observe what your Inner Being knows. Tell it the way you want it.

_____

_____

_____

_____

_____

_____

_____

_____

_____

_____

_____

_____

_____

_____

_____

_____

_____

_____

_____

_____

_____

_____

_____

_____

Identify. Isolate. Calibrate.

Identify

Isolate

Calibrate

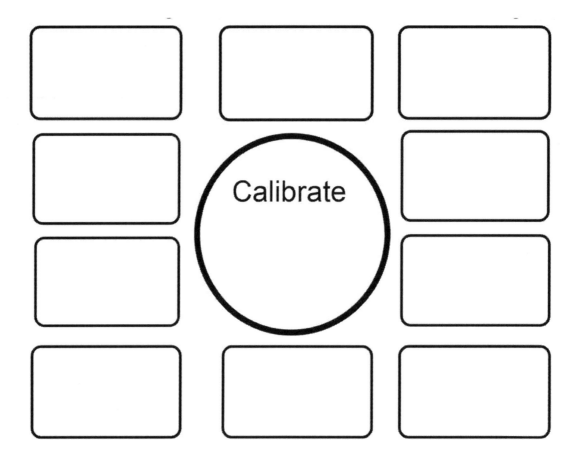

Calibrate

Get out ahead of it. Calibrate!

What is your point of attraction? Point in the direction of what you want.
Observe what your Inner Being knows. Tell it the way you want it.

_____

_____

_____

_____

_____

_____

_____

_____

_____

_____

_____

_____

_____

_____

_____

_____

_____

_____

_____

_____

_____

_____

_____

Identify. Isolate. Calibrate.

Identify

Isolate

Calibrate

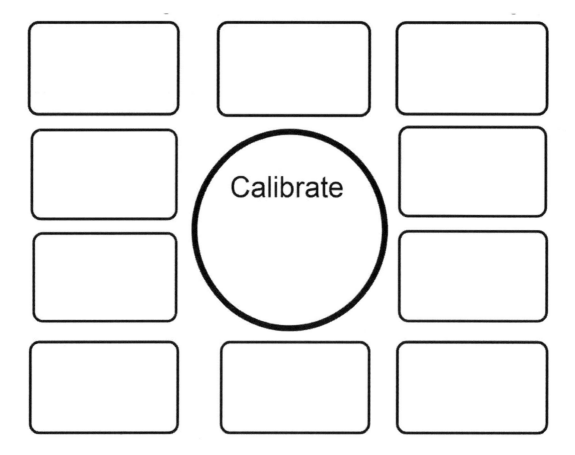

Get out ahead of it. Calibrate!

What is your point of attraction? Point in the direction of what you want.
Observe what your Inner Being knows. Tell it the way you want it.

_____
_____
_____
_____
_____
_____
_____
_____
_____
_____
_____
_____
_____
_____
_____
_____
_____
_____
_____
_____
_____
_____
_____
_____

Identify. Isolate. Calibrate.

Identify

Isolate

Calibrate

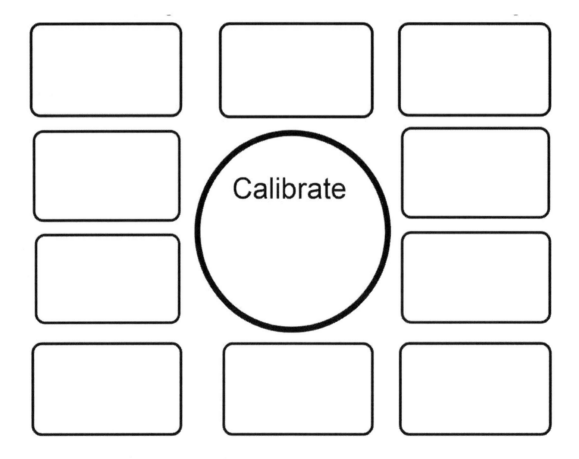

Get out ahead of it. Calibrate!

What is your point of attraction? Point in the direction of what you want.
Observe what your Inner Being knows. Tell it the way you want it.

_____

_____

_____

_____

_____

_____

_____

_____

_____

_____

_____

_____

_____

_____

_____

_____

_____

_____

_____

_____

_____

_____

_____

_____

Identify. Isolate. Calibrate.

Identify

Isolate

Calibrate

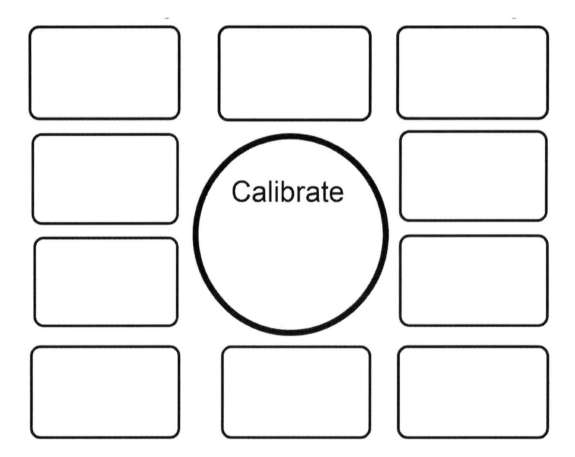

Get out ahead of it. Calibrate!

What is your point of attraction? Point in the direction of what you want.
Observe what your Inner Being knows. Tell it the way you want it.

_____

_____

_____

_____

_____

_____

_____

_____

_____

_____

_____

_____

_____

_____

_____

_____

_____

_____

_____

_____

_____

_____

_____

_____

Identify. Isolate. Calibrate.

Identify

Isolate

Calibrate

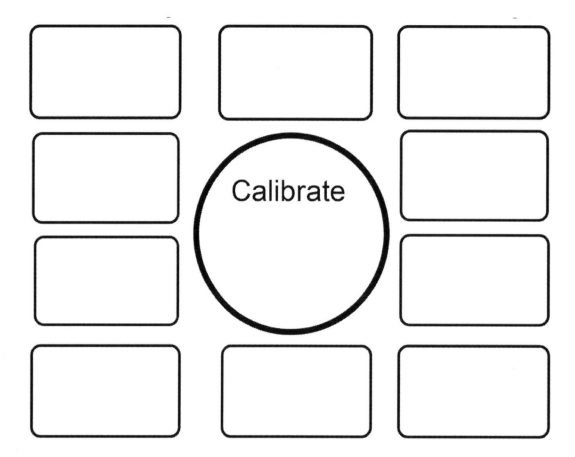

Get out ahead of it. Calibrate!

What is your point of attraction? Point in the direction of what you want.
Observe what your Inner Being knows. Tell it the way you want it.

_____

_____

_____

_____

_____

_____

_____

_____

_____

_____

_____

_____

_____

_____

_____

_____

_____

_____

_____

_____

_____

_____

_____

_____

_____

_____

Identify. Isolate. Calibrate.

Identify

Isolate

Calibrate

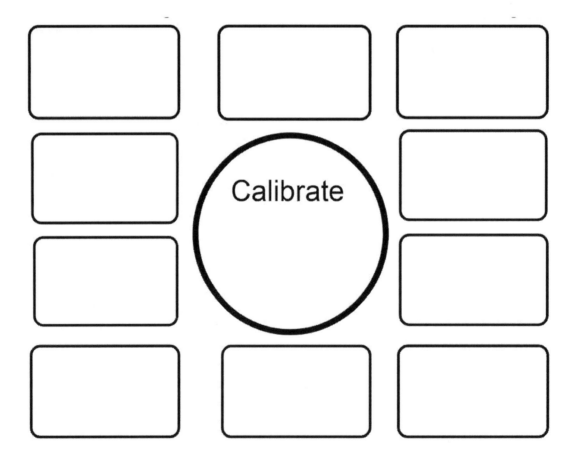

Calibrate

Get out ahead of it. Calibrate!

What is your point of attraction? Point in the direction of what you want.
Observe what your Inner Being knows. Tell it the way you want it.

_____

_____

_____

_____

_____

_____

_____

_____

_____

_____

_____

_____

_____

_____

_____

_____

_____

_____

_____

_____

_____

_____

_____

_____

Identify. Isolate. Calibrate.

Identify

Isolate

Calibrate

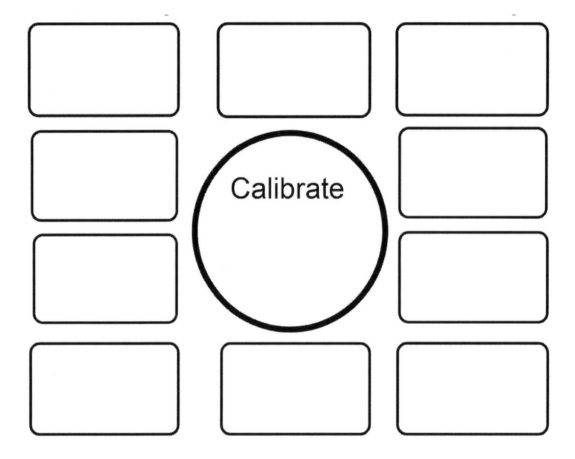

Get out ahead of it. Calibrate!

What is your point of attraction? Point in the direction of what you want.
Observe what your Inner Being knows. Tell it the way you want it.

_____

_____

_____

_____

_____

_____

_____

_____

_____

_____

_____

_____

_____

_____

_____

_____

_____

_____

_____

_____

_____

_____

_____

_____

Identify. Isolate. Calibrate.

Identify

Isolate

Calibrate

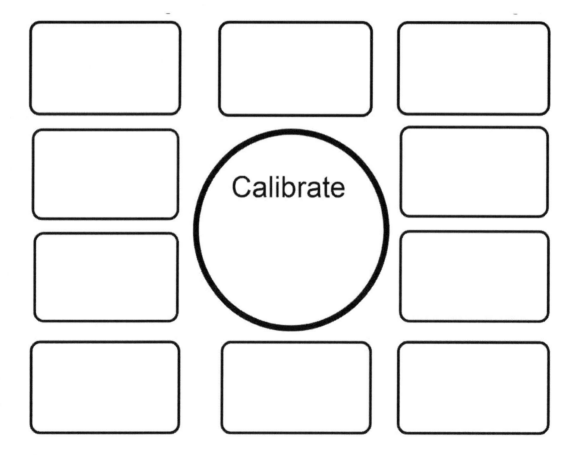
Calibrate

Get out ahead of it. Calibrate!

What is your point of attraction? Point in the direction of what you want.
Observe what your Inner Being knows. Tell it the way you want it.

_____

_____

_____

_____

_____

_____

_____

_____

_____

_____

_____

_____

_____

_____

_____

_____

_____

_____

_____

_____

_____

_____

_____

_____

_____

_____

Identify. Isolate. Calibrate.

Identify

Isolate

Calibrate

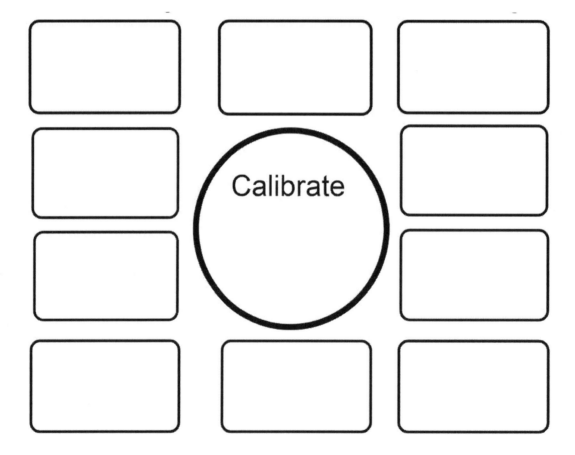

Get out ahead of it. Calibrate!

What is your point of attraction? Point in the direction of what you want.
Observe what your Inner Being knows. Tell it the way you want it.

_____

_____

_____

_____

_____

_____

_____

_____

_____

_____

_____

_____

_____

_____

_____

_____

_____

_____

_____

_____

_____

_____

_____

_____

Identify. Isolate. Calibrate.

Identify

Isolate

Calibrate

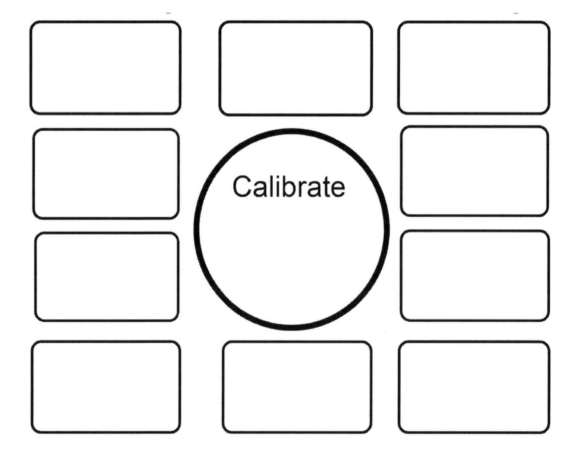

Get out ahead of it. Calibrate!

What is your point of attraction? Point in the direction of what you want.
Observe what your Inner Being knows. Tell it the way you want it.

_____

_____

_____

_____

_____

_____

_____

_____

_____

_____

_____

_____

_____

_____

_____

_____

_____

_____

_____

_____

_____

_____

_____

Identify. Isolate. Calibrate.

Identify

Isolate

Calibrate

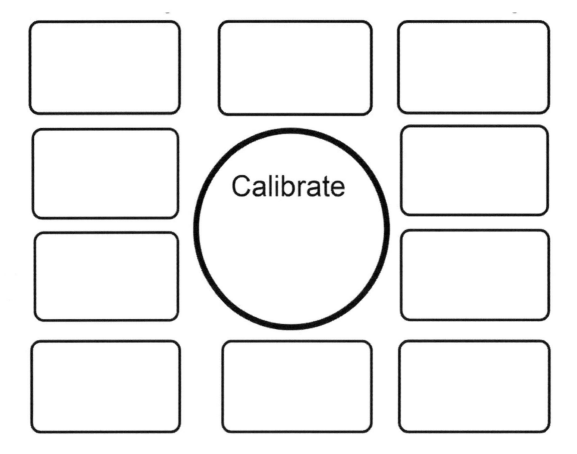

Get out ahead of it. Calibrate!

What is your point of attraction? Point in the direction of what you want.
Observe what your Inner Being knows. Tell it the way you want it.

_____

_____

_____

_____

_____

_____

_____

_____

_____

_____

_____

_____

_____

_____

_____

_____

_____

_____

_____

_____

_____

_____

_____

Identify. Isolate. Calibrate.

Identify

Isolate

Calibrate

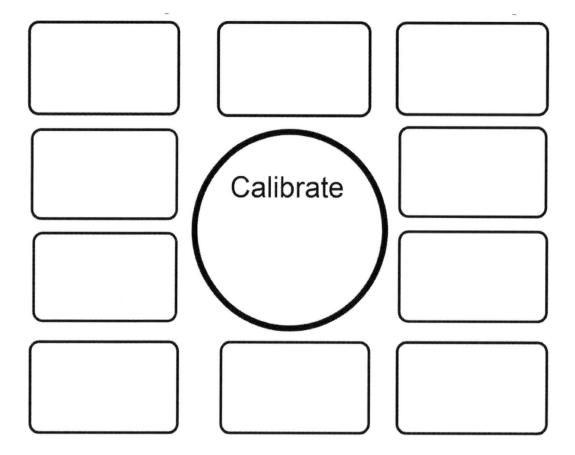

Get out ahead of it. Calibrate!

What is your point of attraction? Point in the direction of what you want.
Observe what your Inner Being knows. Tell it the way you want it.

_____

_____

_____

_____

_____

_____

_____

_____

_____

_____

_____

_____

_____

_____

_____

_____

_____

_____

_____

_____

_____

_____

_____

_____

Identify. Isolate. Calibrate.

Identify

Isolate

Calibrate

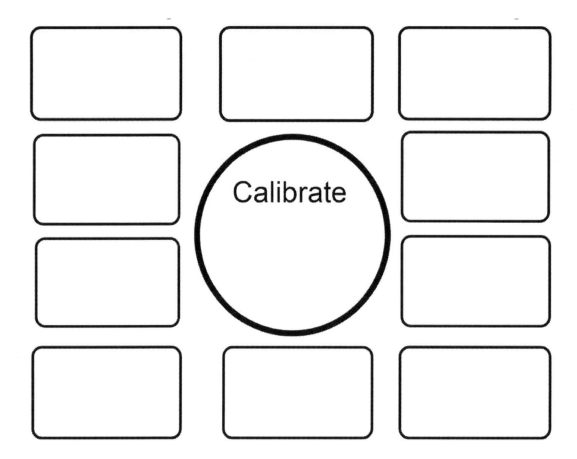

Calibrate

Get out ahead of it. Calibrate!

What is your point of attraction? Point in the direction of what you want.
Observe what your Inner Being knows. Tell it the way you want it.

_____

_____

_____

_____

_____

_____

_____

_____

_____

_____

_____

_____

_____

_____

_____

_____

_____

_____

_____

_____

_____

_____

_____

_____

Identify. Isolate. Calibrate.

Identify

Isolate

Calibrate

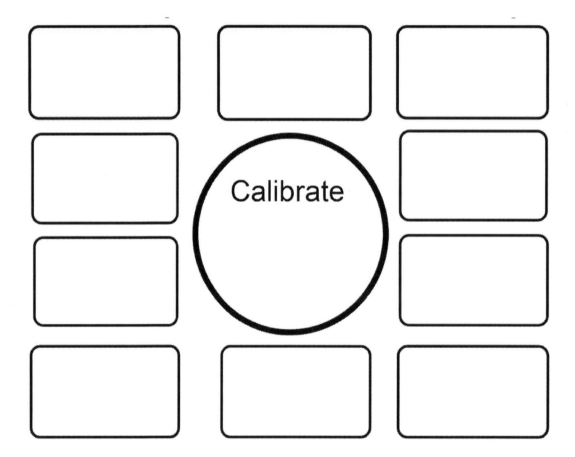

Calibrate

Get out ahead of it. Calibrate!

What is your point of attraction? Point in the direction of what you want.
Observe what your Inner Being knows. Tell it the way you want it.

_____

_____

_____

_____

_____

_____

_____

_____

_____

_____

_____

_____

_____

_____

_____

_____

_____

_____

_____

_____

_____

_____

_____

_____

_____

Identify. Isolate. Calibrate.

Identify

Isolate

Calibrate

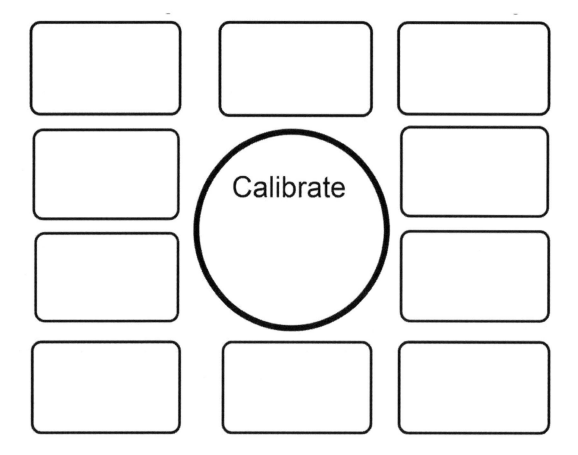

Calibrate

Get out ahead of it. Calibrate!

What is your point of attraction? Point in the direction of what you want.
Observe what your Inner Being knows. Tell it the way you want it.

_____

_____

_____

_____

_____

_____

_____

_____

_____

_____

_____

_____

_____

_____

_____

_____

_____

_____

_____

_____

_____

_____

_____

_____

_____

_____

Identify. Isolate. Calibrate.

Identify

Isolate

Calibrate

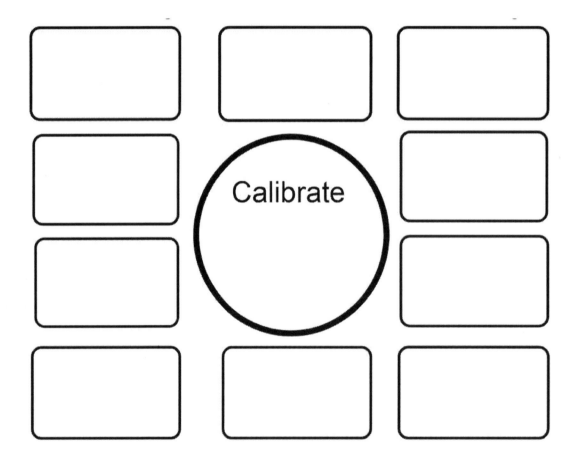

Calibrate

Get out ahead of it. Calibrate!

What is your point of attraction? Point in the direction of what you want.
Observe what your Inner Being knows. Tell it the way you want it.

_____

_____

_____

_____

_____

_____

_____

_____

_____

_____

_____

_____

_____

_____

_____

_____

_____

_____

_____

_____

_____

_____

_____

_____

_____

Identify. Isolate. Calibrate.

Identify

Isolate

Calibrate

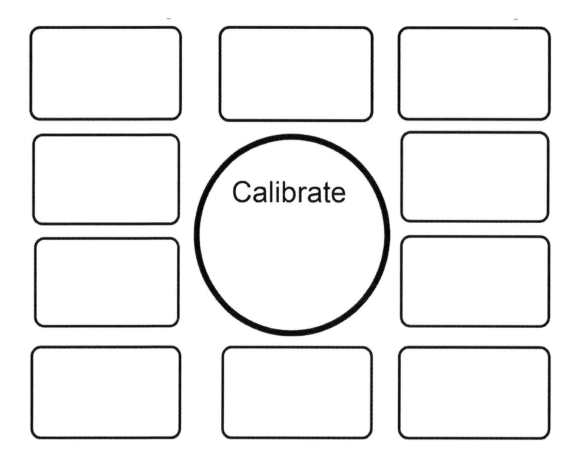

Get out ahead of it. Calibrate!

What is your point of attraction? Point in the direction of what you want.
Observe what your Inner Being knows. Tell it the way you want it.

_____

_____

_____

_____

_____

_____

_____

_____

_____

_____

_____

_____

_____

_____

_____

_____

_____

_____

_____

_____

_____

_____

_____

_____

Identify. Isolate. Calibrate.

Identify

Isolate

Calibrate

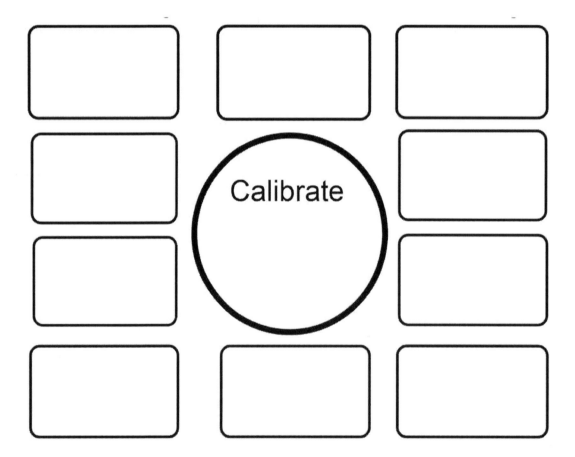

Get out ahead of it. Calibrate!

What is your point of attraction? Point in the direction of what you want.
Observe what your Inner Being knows. Tell it the way you want it.

_____

_____

_____

_____

_____

_____

_____

_____

_____

_____

_____

_____

_____

_____

_____

_____

_____

_____

_____

_____

_____

_____

_____

_____

_____

_____

Identify. Isolate. Calibrate.

Identify

Isolate

Calibrate

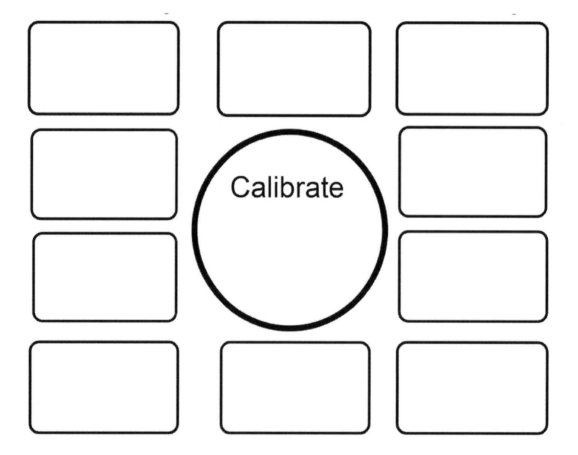

Get out ahead of it. Calibrate!

What is your point of attraction? Point in the direction of what you want.
Observe what your Inner Being knows. Tell it the way you want it.

_____

_____

_____

_____

_____

_____

_____

_____

_____

_____

_____

_____

_____

_____

_____

_____

_____

_____

_____

_____

_____

_____

_____

_____

Identify. Isolate. Calibrate.

Identify

Isolate

Calibrate

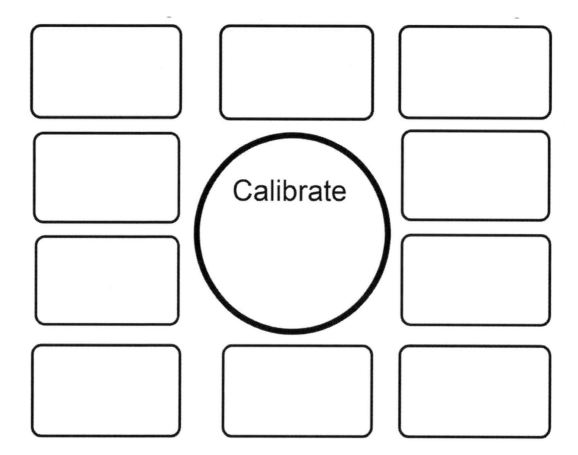

Get out ahead of it. Calibrate!

What is your point of attraction? Point in the direction of what you want.
Observe what your Inner Being knows. Tell it the way you want it.

_____

_____

_____

_____

_____

_____

_____

_____

_____

_____

_____

_____

_____

_____

_____

_____

_____

_____

_____

_____

_____

_____

_____

_____

Identify. Isolate. Calibrate.

Identify

Isolate

Calibrate

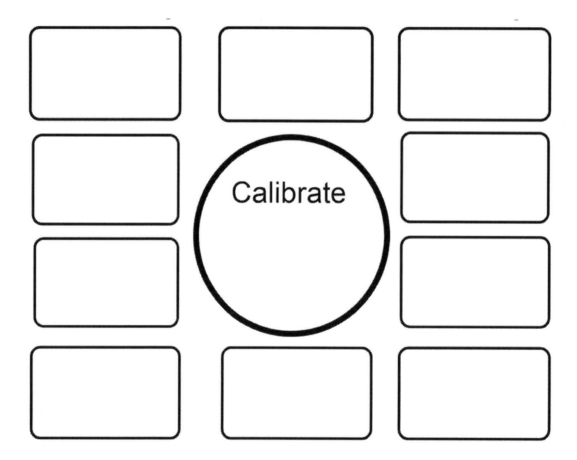

Get out ahead of it. Calibrate!

What is your point of attraction? Point in the direction of what you want.
Observe what your Inner Being knows. Tell it the way you want it.

_____

_____

_____

_____

_____

_____

_____

_____

_____

_____

_____

_____

_____

_____

_____

_____

_____

_____

_____

_____

_____

_____

_____

_____

_____

_____

_____

Identify. Isolate. Calibrate.

Identify

Isolate

Calibrate

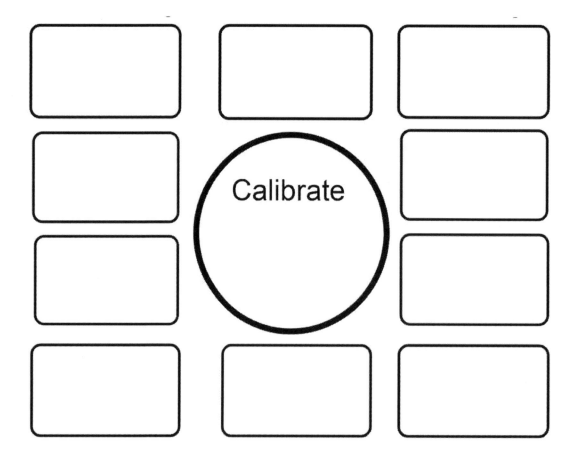

Get out ahead of it. Calibrate!

What is your point of attraction? Point in the direction of what you want.
Observe what your Inner Being knows. Tell it the way you want it.

_____

_____

_____

_____

_____

_____

_____

_____

_____

_____

_____

_____

_____

_____

_____

_____

_____

_____

_____

_____

_____

_____

_____

_____

_____

Identify. Isolate. Calibrate.

Identify

Isolate

Calibrate

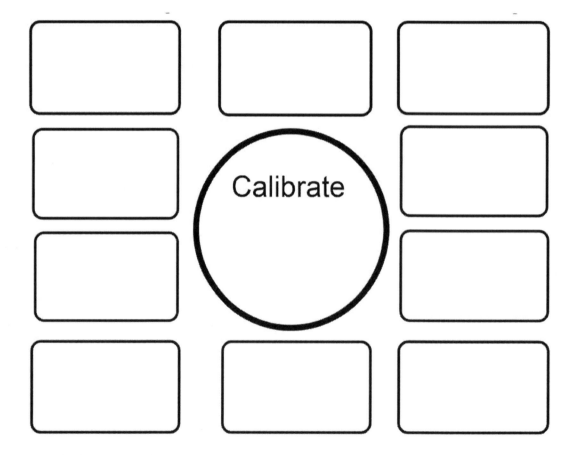

Get out ahead of it. Calibrate!

What is your point of attraction? Point in the direction of what you want.
Observe what your Inner Being knows. Tell it the way you want it.

_____

_____

_____

_____

_____

_____

_____

_____

_____

_____

_____

_____

_____

_____

_____

_____

_____

_____

_____

_____

_____

_____

_____

_____

Identify. Isolate. Calibrate.

Identify

Isolate

Calibrate

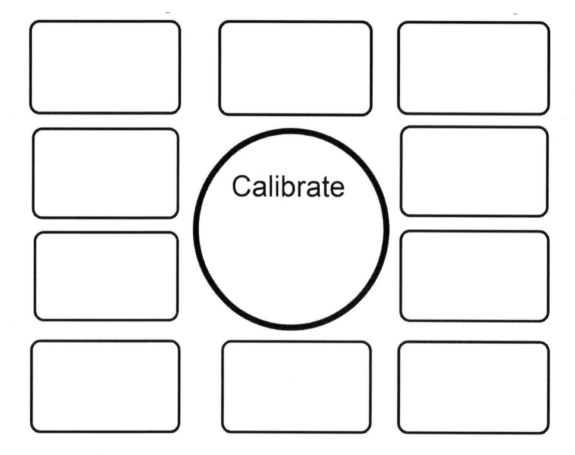

Get out ahead of it. Calibrate!

What is your point of attraction? Point in the direction of what you want.
Observe what your Inner Being knows. Tell it the way you want it.

_____

_____

_____

_____

_____

_____

_____

_____

_____

_____

_____

_____

_____

_____

_____

_____

_____

_____

_____

_____

_____

_____

_____

_____

Identify. Isolate. Calibrate.

Identify

Isolate

Calibrate

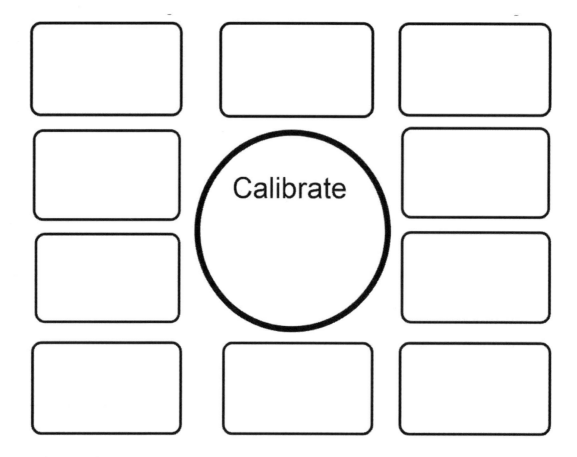

Calibrate

Get out ahead of it. Calibrate!

What is your point of attraction? Point in the direction of what you want.
Observe what your Inner Being knows. Tell it the way you want it.

_____

_____

_____

_____

_____

_____

_____

_____

_____

_____

_____

_____

_____

_____

_____

_____

_____

_____

_____

_____

_____

_____

_____

_____

Identify. Isolate. Calibrate.

Identify

Isolate

Calibrate

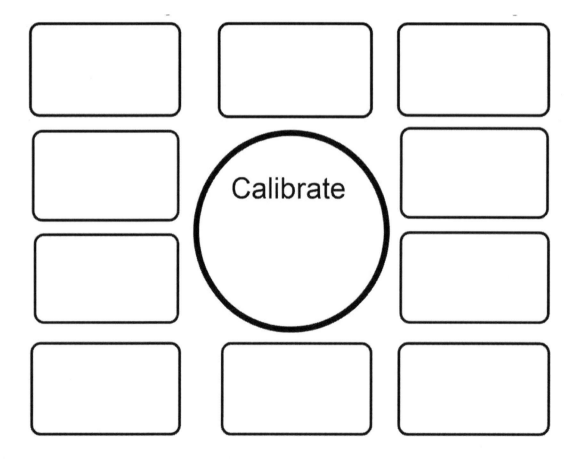

Get out ahead of it. Calibrate!

What is your point of attraction? Point in the direction of what you want.
Observe what your Inner Being knows. Tell it the way you want it.

_____

_____

_____

_____

_____

_____

_____

_____

_____

_____

_____

_____

_____

_____

_____

_____

_____

_____

_____

_____

_____

_____

_____

_____

_____

Identify. Isolate. Calibrate.

Identify

Isolate

Calibrate

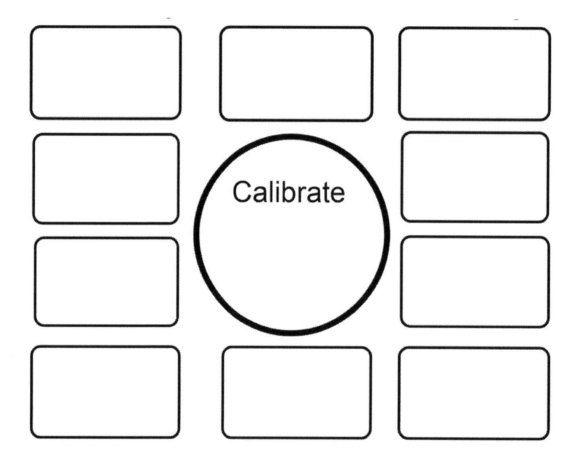

Get out ahead of it. Calibrate!

What is your point of attraction? Point in the direction of what you want.
Observe what your Inner Being knows. Tell it the way you want it.

_____

_____

_____

_____

_____

_____

_____

_____

_____

_____

_____

_____

_____

_____

_____

_____

_____

_____

_____

_____

_____

_____

_____

_____

Identify. Isolate. Calibrate.

Identify

Isolate

Calibrate

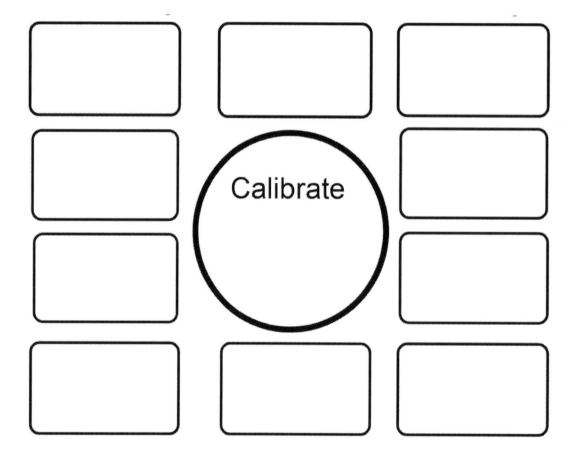

Get out ahead of it. Calibrate!

What is your point of attraction? Point in the direction of what you want.
Observe what your Inner Being knows. Tell it the way you want it.

_____

_____

_____

_____

_____

_____

_____

_____

_____

_____

_____

_____

_____

_____

_____

_____

_____

_____

_____

_____

_____

_____

_____

_____

Identify. Isolate. Calibrate.

Identify

Isolate

Calibrate

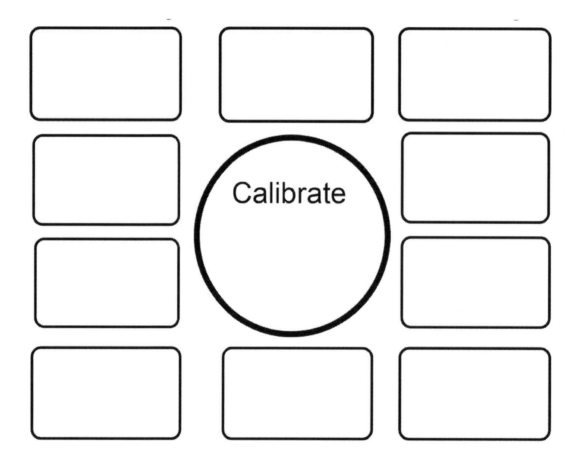

Get out ahead of it. Calibrate!

What is your point of attraction? Point in the direction of what you want.
Observe what your Inner Being knows. Tell it the way you want it.

_____

_____

_____

_____

_____

_____

_____

_____

_____

_____

_____

_____

_____

_____

_____

_____

_____

_____

_____

_____

_____

_____

_____

_____

_____

Identify. Isolate. Calibrate.

Identify

Isolate

Calibrate

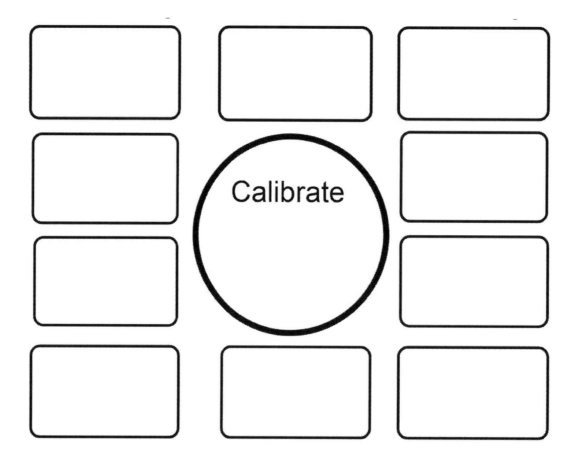

Get out ahead of it. Calibrate!

What is your point of attraction? Point in the direction of what you want.
Observe what your Inner Being knows. Tell it the way you want it.

_____

_____

_____

_____

_____

_____

_____

_____

_____

_____

_____

_____

_____

_____

_____

_____

_____

_____

_____

_____

_____

_____

_____

_____

Identify. Isolate. Calibrate.

Identify

Isolate

Calibrate

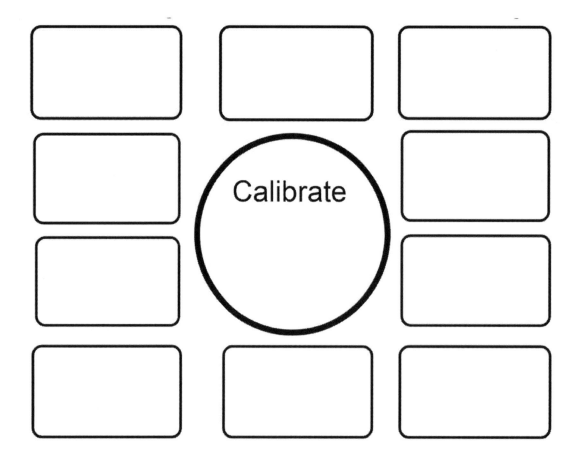

Get out ahead of it. Calibrate!

What is your point of attraction? Point in the direction of what you want.
Observe what your Inner Being knows. Tell it the way you want it.

_____

_____

_____

_____

_____

_____

_____

_____

_____

_____

_____

_____

_____

_____

_____

_____

_____

_____

_____

_____

_____

_____

_____

_____

_____

_____

Identify. Isolate. Calibrate.

Identify

Isolate

Calibrate

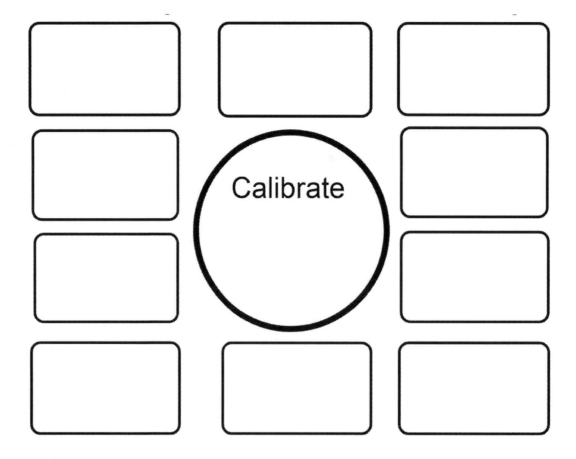

Calibrate

Get out ahead of it. Calibrate!

What is your point of attraction? Point in the direction of what you want.
Observe what your Inner Being knows. Tell it the way you want it.

_____

_____

_____

_____

_____

_____

_____

_____

_____

_____

_____

_____

_____

_____

_____

_____

_____

_____

_____

_____

_____

_____

_____

_____

Identify. Isolate. Calibrate.

Identify

Isolate

Calibrate

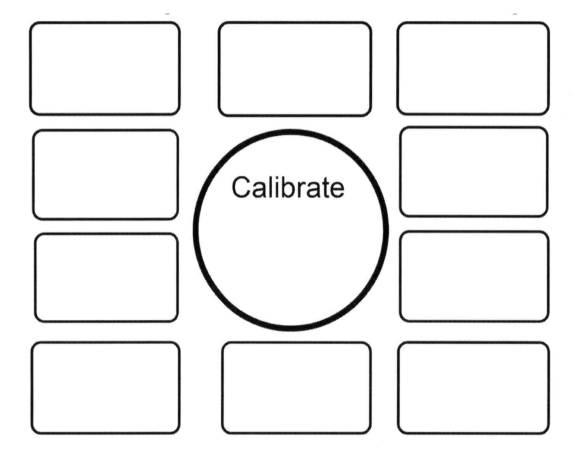

Get out ahead of it. Calibrate!

What is your point of attraction? Point in the direction of what you want.
Observe what your Inner Being knows. Tell it the way you want it.

_____

_____

_____

_____

_____

_____

_____

_____

_____

_____

_____

_____

_____

_____

_____

_____

_____

_____

_____

_____

_____

_____

_____

Identify. Isolate. Calibrate.

Identify

Isolate

Calibrate

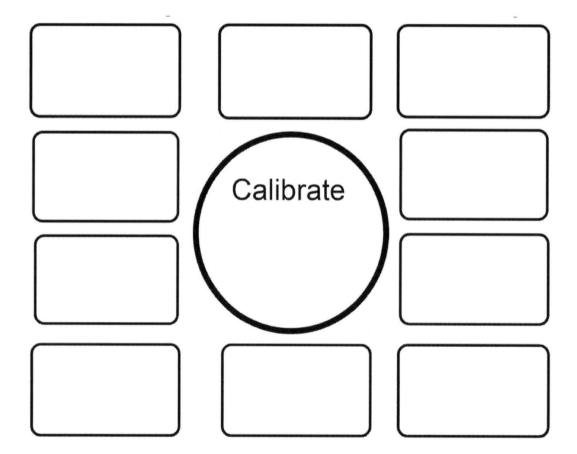

Get out ahead of it. Calibrate!

What is your point of attraction? Point in the direction of what you want.
Observe what your Inner Being knows. Tell it the way you want it.

_____

_____

_____

_____

_____

_____

_____

_____

_____

_____

_____

_____

_____

_____

_____

_____

_____

_____

_____

_____

_____

_____

_____

Identify. Isolate. Calibrate.

Identify

Isolate

Calibrate

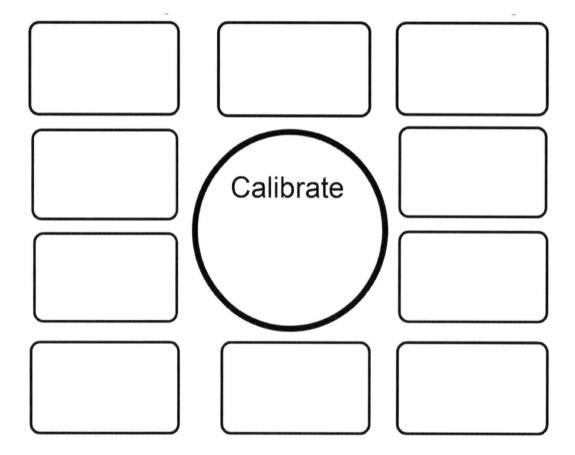

Get out ahead of it. Calibrate!

What is your point of attraction? Point in the direction of what you want. Observe what your Inner Being knows. Tell it the way you want it.

_____

_____

_____

_____

_____

_____

_____

_____

_____

_____

_____

_____

_____

_____

_____

_____

_____

_____

_____

_____

_____

_____

_____

_____

Identify. Isolate. Calibrate.

Identify

Isolate

Calibrate

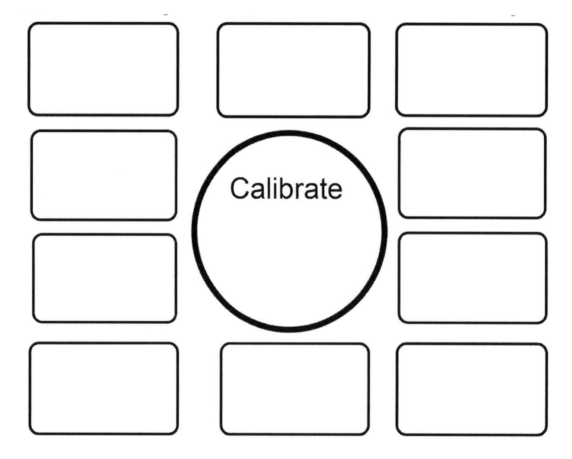

Get out ahead of it. Calibrate!

What is your point of attraction? Point in the direction of what you want.
Observe what your Inner Being knows. Tell it the way you want it.

_____
_____
_____
_____
_____
_____
_____
_____
_____
_____
_____
_____
_____
_____
_____
_____
_____
_____
_____
_____
_____

Identify. Isolate. Calibrate.

Identify

Isolate

Calibrate

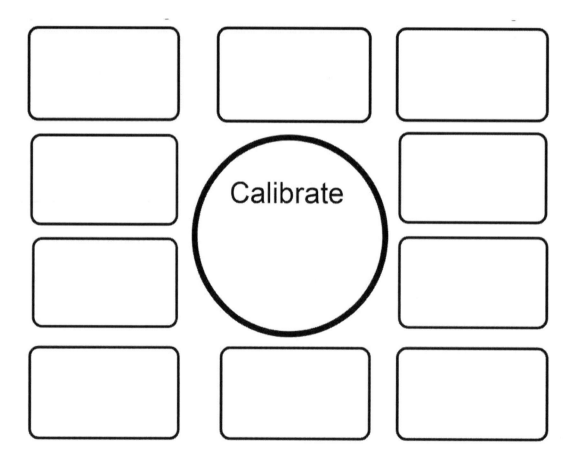

Get out ahead of it. Calibrate!

What is your point of attraction? Point in the direction of what you want.
Observe what your Inner Being knows. Tell it the way you want it.

_____

_____

_____

_____

_____

_____

_____

_____

_____

_____

_____

_____

_____

_____

_____

_____

_____

_____

_____

_____

_____

_____

_____

_____

Identify. Isolate. Calibrate.

Identify

Isolate

Calibrate

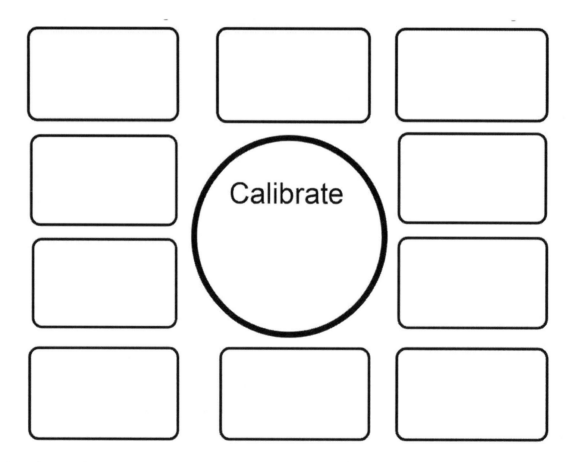

Get out ahead of it. Calibrate!

What is your point of attraction? Point in the direction of what you want.
Observe what your Inner Being knows. Tell it the way you want it.

_____

_____

_____

_____

_____

_____

_____

_____

_____

_____

_____

_____

_____

_____

_____

_____

_____

_____

_____

_____

_____

_____

_____

_____

Identify. Isolate. Calibrate.

Identify

Isolate

Calibrate

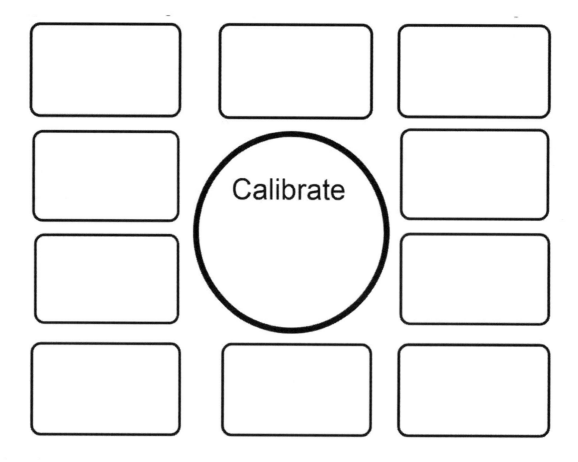

Get out ahead of it. Calibrate!

What is your point of attraction? Point in the direction of what you want.
Observe what your Inner Being knows. Tell it the way you want it.

_____

_____

_____

_____

_____

_____

_____

_____

_____

_____

_____

_____

_____

_____

_____

_____

_____

_____

_____

_____

_____

_____

_____

Identify. Isolate. Calibrate.

Identify

Isolate

Calibrate

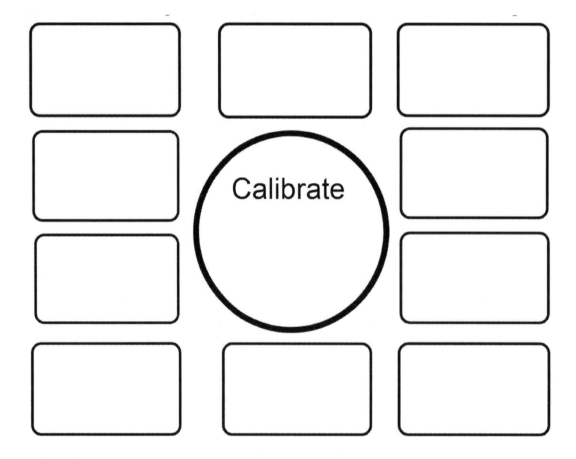

Get out ahead of it. Calibrate!

What is your point of attraction? Point in the direction of what you want.
Observe what your Inner Being knows. Tell it the way you want it.

_____

_____

_____

_____

_____

_____

_____

_____

_____

_____

_____

_____

_____

_____

_____

_____

_____

_____

_____

_____

_____

_____

_____

_____

_____

Identify. Isolate. Calibrate.

Identify

Isolate

Calibrate

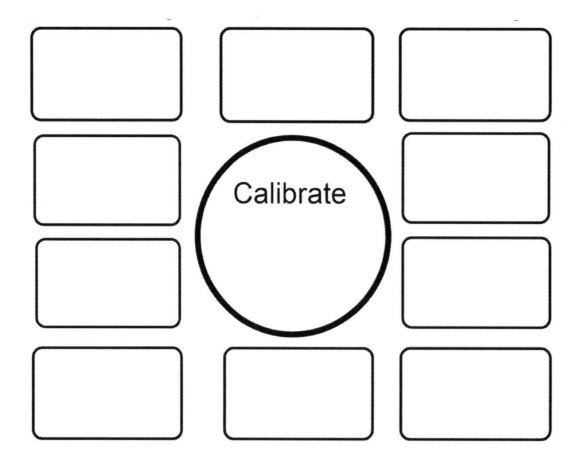

Calibrate

Get out ahead of it. Calibrate!

What is your point of attraction? Point in the direction of what you want.
Observe what your Inner Being knows. Tell it the way you want it.

_____

_____

_____

_____

_____

_____

_____

_____

_____

_____

_____

_____

_____

_____

_____

_____

_____

_____

_____

_____

_____

_____

_____

_____

Identify. Isolate. Calibrate.

Identify

Isolate

Calibrate

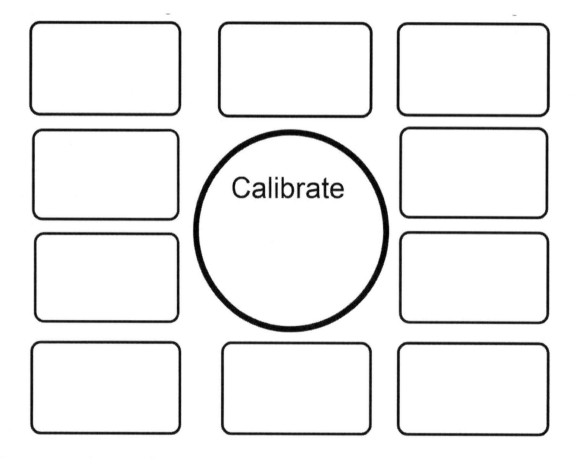

Get out ahead of it. Calibrate!

What is your point of attraction? Point in the direction of what you want.
Observe what your Inner Being knows. Tell it the way you want it.

_____

_____

_____

_____

_____

_____

_____

_____

_____

_____

_____

_____

_____

_____

_____

_____

_____

_____

_____

_____

_____

_____

_____

_____

_____

Identify. Isolate. Calibrate.

Identify

Isolate

Calibrate

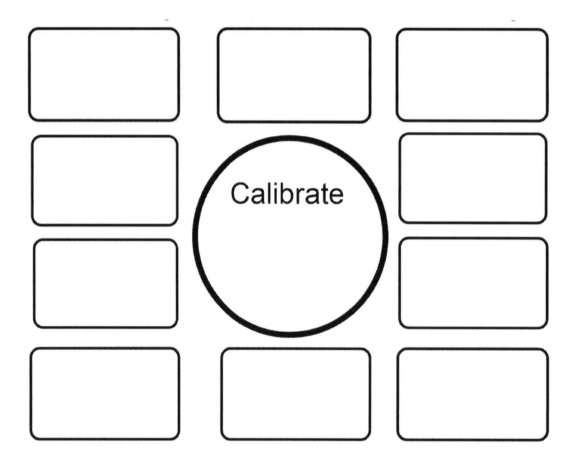

Get out ahead of it. Calibrate!

What is your point of attraction? Point in the direction of what you want.
Observe what your Inner Being knows. Tell it the way you want it.

_____

_____

_____

_____

_____

_____

_____

_____

_____

_____

_____

_____

_____

_____

_____

_____

_____

_____

_____

_____

_____

_____

_____

Identify. Isolate. Calibrate.

Identify

Isolate

Calibrate

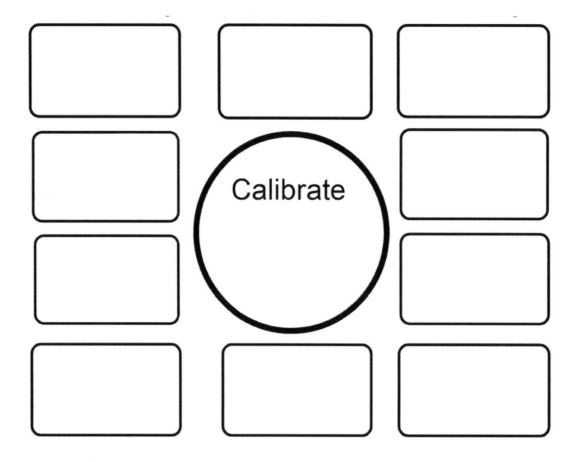

Get out ahead of it. Calibrate!

What is your point of attraction? Point in the direction of what you want.
Observe what your Inner Being knows. Tell it the way you want it.

_____

_____

_____

_____

_____

_____

_____

_____

_____

_____

_____

_____

_____

_____

_____

_____

_____

_____

_____

_____

_____

_____

Identify. Isolate. Calibrate.

Identify

Isolate

Calibrate

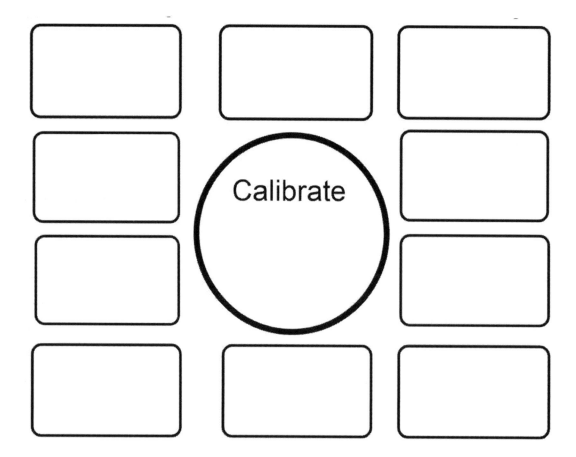

Get out ahead of it. Calibrate!

What is your point of attraction? Point in the direction of what you want.
Observe what your Inner Being knows. Tell it the way you want it.

_____

_____

_____

_____

_____

_____

_____

_____

_____

_____

_____

_____

_____

_____

_____

_____

_____

_____

_____

_____

_____

_____

_____

Identify. Isolate. Calibrate.

Identify

Isolate

Calibrate

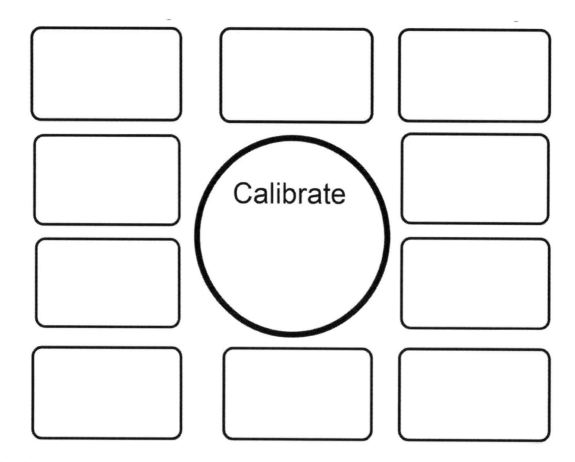

Get out ahead of it. Calibrate!

What is your point of attraction? Point in the direction of what you want.
Observe what your Inner Being knows. Tell it the way you want it.

_____

_____

_____

_____

_____

_____

_____

_____

_____

_____

_____

_____

_____

_____

_____

_____

_____

_____

_____

_____

_____

_____

_____

Identify. Isolate. Calibrate.

Identify

Isolate

Calibrate

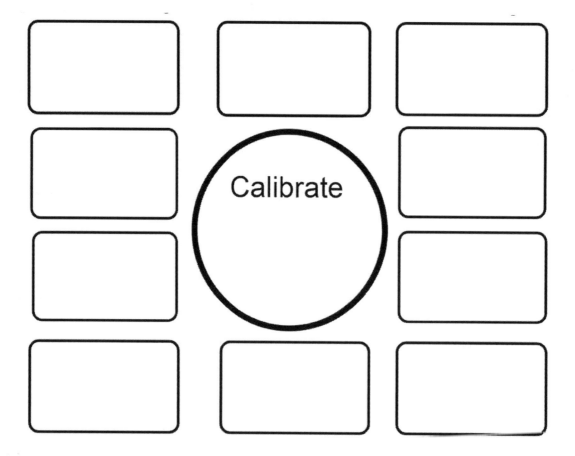

Get out ahead of it. Calibrate!

What is your point of attraction? Point in the direction of what you want.
Observe what your Inner Being knows. Tell it the way you want it.

_____

_____

_____

_____

_____

_____

_____

_____

_____

_____

_____

_____

_____

_____

_____

_____

_____

_____

_____

_____

_____

_____

Identify. Isolate. Calibrate.

Identify

Isolate

Calibrate

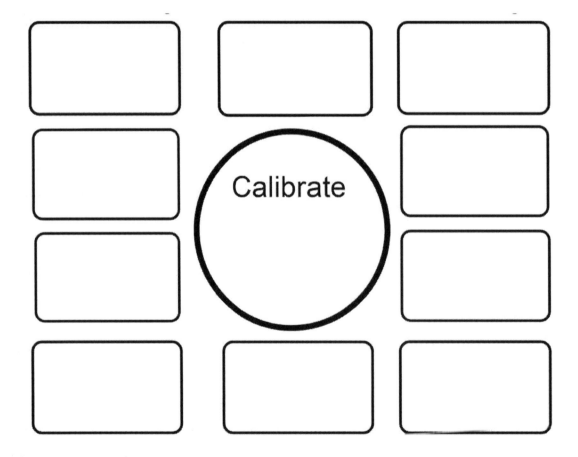

Get out ahead of it. Calibrate!

What is your point of attraction? Point in the direction of what you want.
Observe what your Inner Being knows. Tell it the way you want it.

_____

_____

_____

_____

_____

_____

_____

_____

_____

_____

_____

_____

_____

_____

_____

_____

_____

_____

_____

_____

_____

_____

_____

_____

Identify. Isolate. Calibrate.

Identify

Isolate

Calibrate

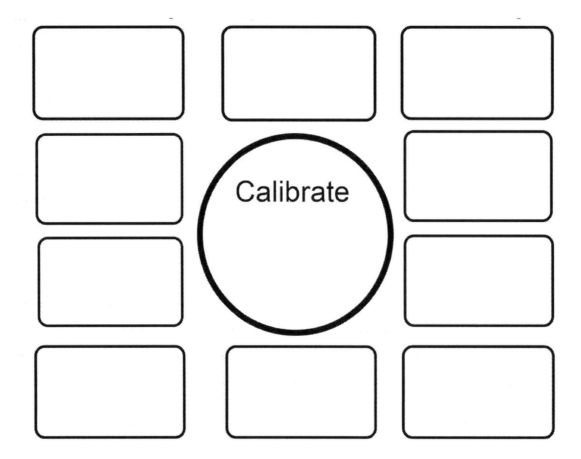

Calibrate

Get out ahead of it. Calibrate!

What is your point of attraction? Point in the direction of what you want. Observe what your Inner Being knows. Tell it the way you want it.

_____

_____

_____

_____

_____

_____

_____

_____

_____

_____

_____

_____

_____

_____

_____

_____

_____

_____

_____

_____

_____

_____

_____

_____

Identify. Isolate. Calibrate.

Identify

Isolate

Calibrate

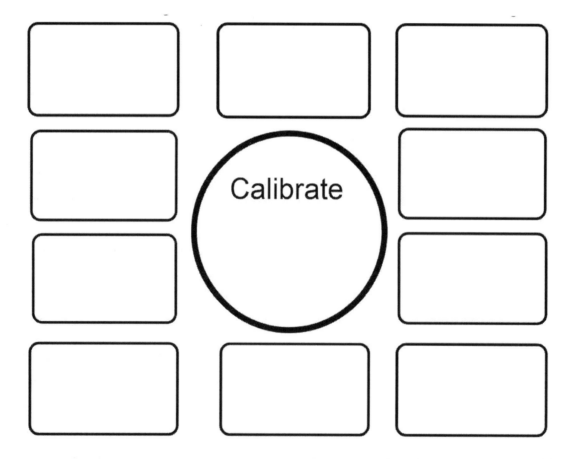

Calibrate

Get out ahead of it. Calibrate!

What is your point of attraction? Point in the direction of what you want.
Observe what your Inner Being knows. Tell it the way you want it.

_____

_____

_____

_____

_____

_____

_____

_____

_____

_____

_____

_____

_____

_____

_____

_____

_____

_____

_____

_____

_____

_____

Identify. Isolate. Calibrate.

Identify

Isolate

Calibrate

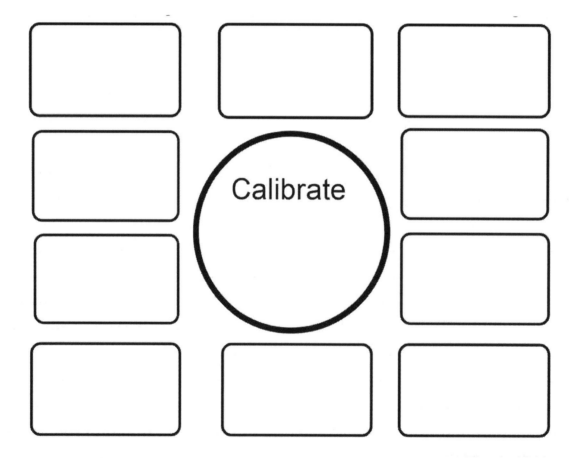

Get out ahead of it. Calibrate!

What is your point of attraction? Point in the direction of what you want.
Observe what your Inner Being knows. Tell it the way you want it.

_____

_____

_____

_____

_____

_____

_____

_____

_____

_____

_____

_____

_____

_____

_____

_____

_____

_____

_____

_____

_____

_____

_____

_____

Identify. Isolate. Calibrate.

Identify

Isolate

Calibrate

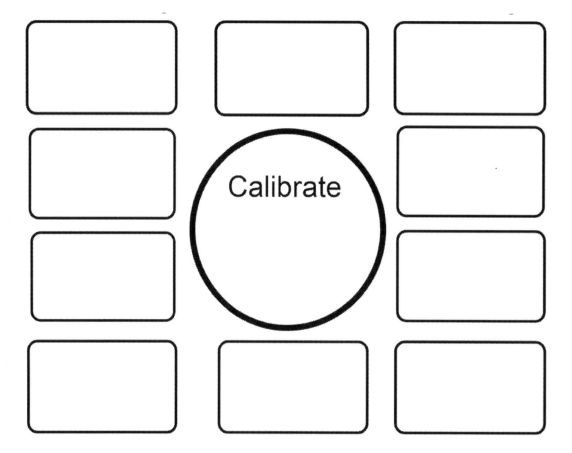

Calibrate

Get out ahead of it. Calibrate!

What is your point of attraction? Point in the direction of what you want.
Observe what your Inner Being knows. Tell it the way you want it.

_____

_____

_____

_____

_____

_____

_____

_____

_____

_____

_____

_____

_____

_____

_____

_____

_____

_____

_____

_____

_____

_____

_____

_____

Identify. Isolate. Calibrate.

Identify

Isolate

Calibrate

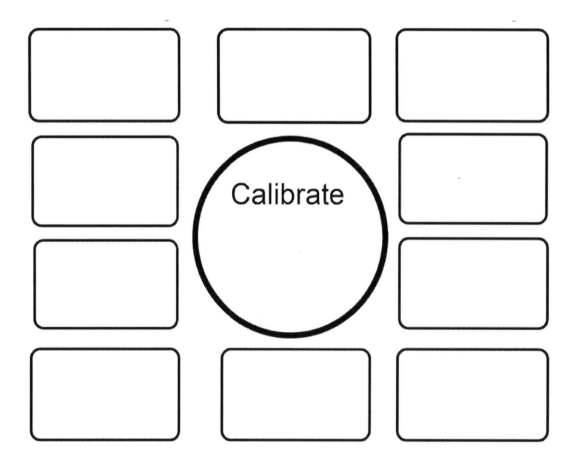

Get out ahead of it. Calibrate!

What is your point of attraction? Point in the direction of what you want.
Observe what your Inner Being knows. Tell it the way you want it.

_____

_____

_____

_____

_____

_____

_____

_____

_____

_____

_____

_____

_____

_____

_____

_____

_____

_____

_____

_____

_____

_____

Identify. Isolate. Calibrate.

Identify

Isolate

Calibrate

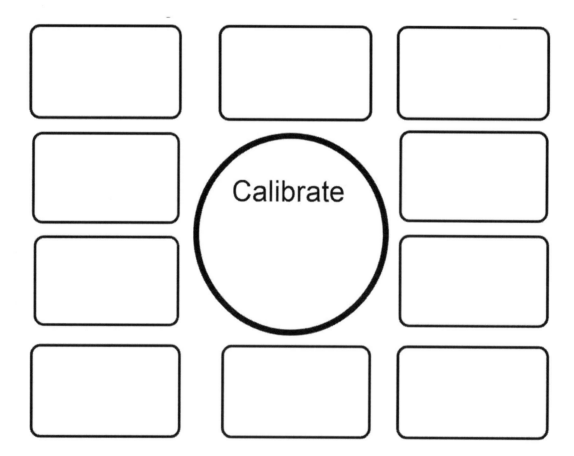

Get out ahead of it. Calibrate!

What is your point of attraction? Point in the direction of what you want.
Observe what your Inner Being knows. Tell it the way you want it.

_____

_____

_____

_____

_____

_____

_____

_____

_____

_____

_____

_____

_____

_____

_____

_____

_____

_____

_____

_____

_____

_____

_____

Identify. Isolate. Calibrate.

Identify

Isolate

Calibrate

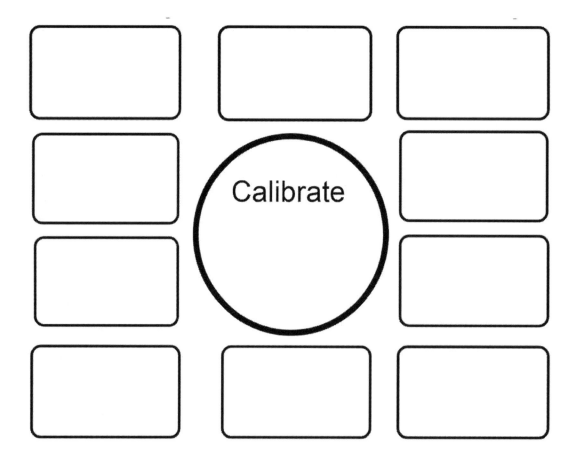

Get out ahead of it. Calibrate!

What is your point of attraction? Point in the direction of what you want.
Observe what your Inner Being knows. Tell it the way you want it.

_____

_____

_____

_____

_____

_____

_____

_____

_____

_____

_____

_____

_____

_____

_____

_____

_____

_____

_____

_____

_____

_____

_____

Identify. Isolate. Calibrate.

Identify

Isolate

Calibrate

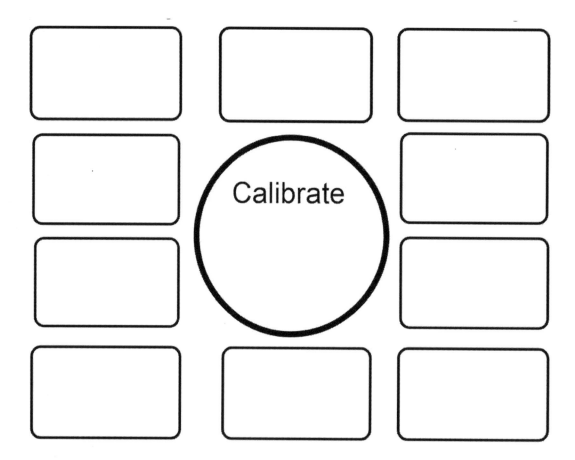

Get out ahead of it. Calibrate!

What is your point of attraction? Point in the direction of what you want.
Observe what your Inner Being knows. Tell it the way you want it.

_____

_____

_____

_____

_____

_____

_____

_____

_____

_____

_____

_____

_____

_____

_____

_____

_____

_____

_____

_____

_____

_____

Identify. Isolate. Calibrate.

Identify

Isolate

Calibrate

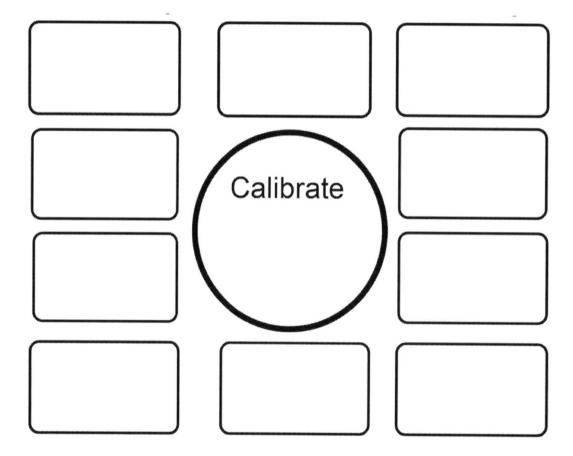

Get out ahead of it. Calibrate!

What is your point of attraction? Point in the direction of what you want.
Observe what your Inner Being knows. Tell it the way you want it.

_____

_____

_____

_____

_____

_____

_____

_____

_____

_____

_____

_____

_____

_____

_____

_____

_____

_____

_____

_____

_____

_____

_____

Identify. Isolate. Calibrate.

Identify

Isolate

Calibrate

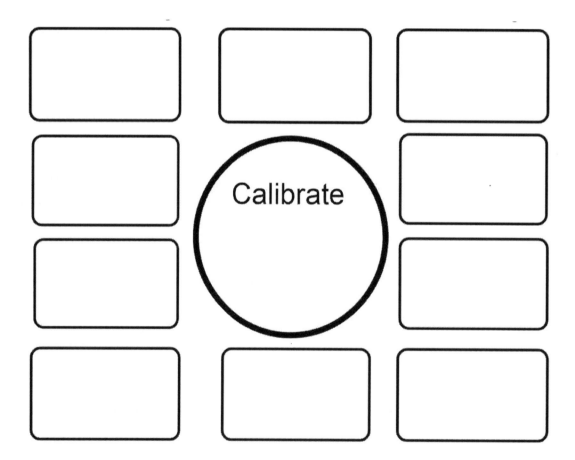

Get out ahead of it. Calibrate!

What is your point of attraction? Point in the direction of what you want.
Observe what your Inner Being knows. Tell it the way you want it.

_____

_____

_____

_____

_____

_____

_____

_____

_____

_____

_____

_____

_____

_____

_____

_____

_____

_____

_____

_____

_____

_____

_____

_____

Identify. Isolate. Calibrate.

Identify

Isolate

Calibrate

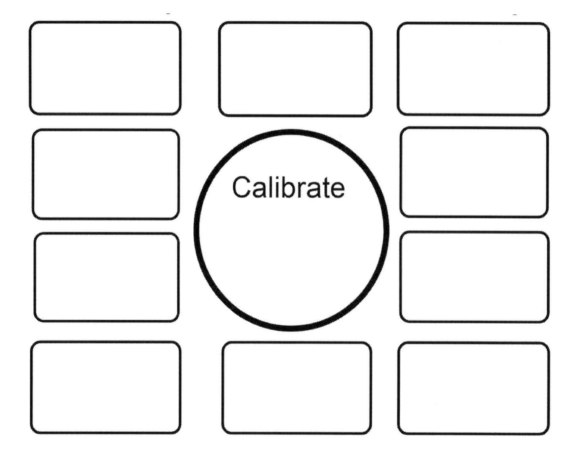

Get out ahead of it. Calibrate!

What is your point of attraction? Point in the direction of what you want.
Observe what your Inner Being knows. Tell it the way you want it.

_____

_____

_____

_____

_____

_____

_____

_____

_____

_____

_____

_____

_____

_____

_____

_____

_____

_____

_____

_____

_____

_____

_____

_____

Identify. Isolate. Calibrate.

Identify

Isolate

Calibrate

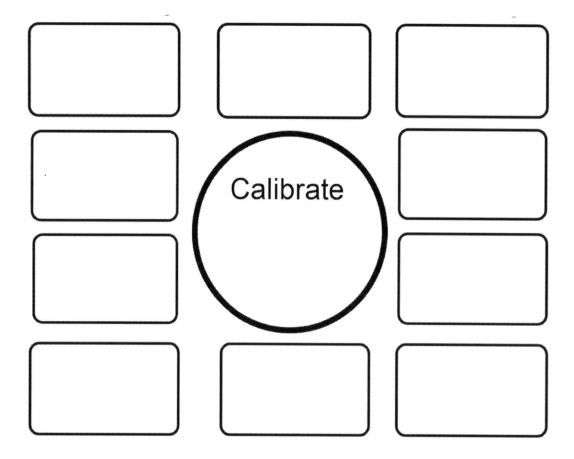

Calibrate

Get out ahead of it. Calibrate!

What is your point of attraction? Point in the direction of what you want.
Observe what your Inner Being knows. Tell it the way you want it.

_____

_____

_____

_____

_____

_____

_____

_____

_____

_____

_____

_____

_____

_____

_____

_____

_____

_____

_____

_____

_____

_____

Identify. Isolate. Calibrate.

Identify

Isolate

Calibrate

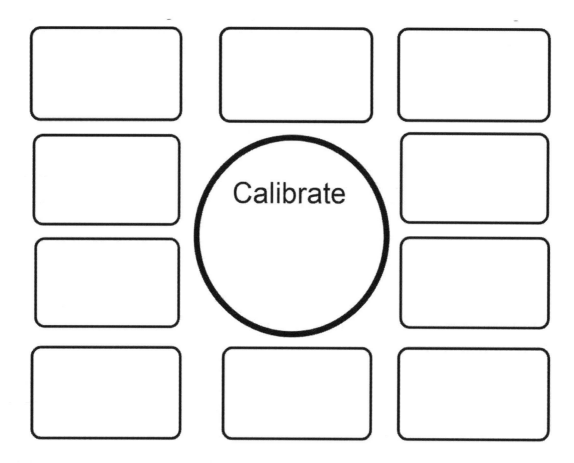

Calibrate

Get out ahead of it. Calibrate!

What is your point of attraction? Point in the direction of what you want.
Observe what your Inner Being knows. Tell it the way you want it.

_____

_____

_____

_____

_____

_____

_____

_____

_____

_____

_____

_____

_____

_____

_____

_____

_____

_____

_____

_____

_____

_____

_____

_____

Identify. Isolate. Calibrate.

Identify

Isolate

Calibrate

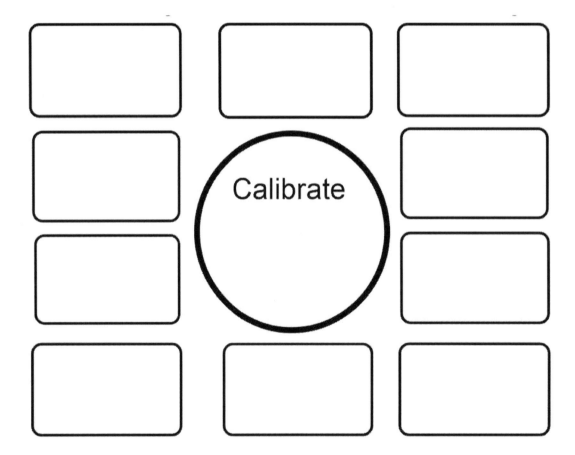

Get out ahead of it. Calibrate!

What is your point of attraction? Point in the direction of what you want.
Observe what your Inner Being knows. Tell it the way you want it.

_____

_____

_____

_____

_____

_____

_____

_____

_____

_____

_____

_____

_____

_____

_____

_____

_____

_____

_____

_____

_____

_____

Identify. Isolate. Calibrate.

Identify

Isolate

Calibrate

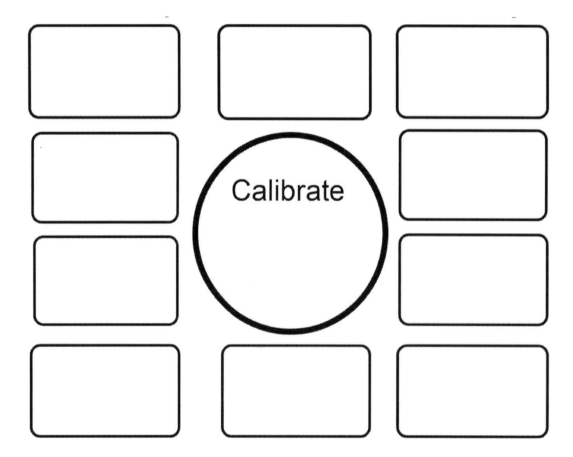

Calibrate

Get out ahead of it. Calibrate!

What is your point of attraction? Point in the direction of what you want.
Observe what your Inner Being knows. Tell it the way you want it.

_____

_____

_____

_____

_____

_____

_____

_____

_____

_____

_____

_____

_____

_____

_____

_____

_____

_____

_____

_____

_____

_____

_____

_____

Identify. Isolate. Calibrate.

Identify

Isolate

Calibrate

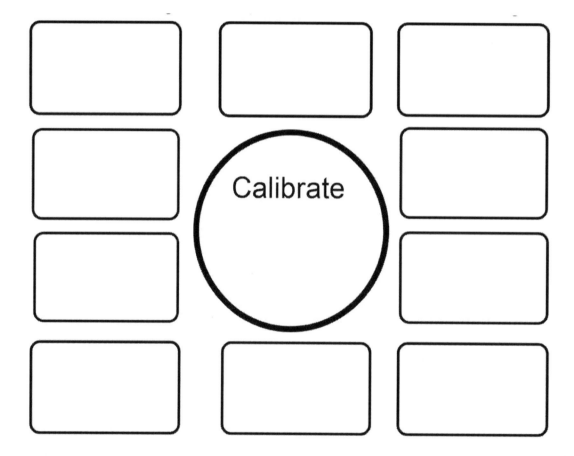

Calibrate

Get out ahead of it. Calibrate!

What is your point of attraction? Point in the direction of what you want.
Observe what your Inner Being knows. Tell it the way you want it.

_____

_____

_____

_____

_____

_____

_____

_____

_____

_____

_____

_____

_____

_____

_____

_____

_____

_____

_____

_____

_____

_____

_____

Identify. Isolate. Calibrate.

Identify

Isolate

Calibrate

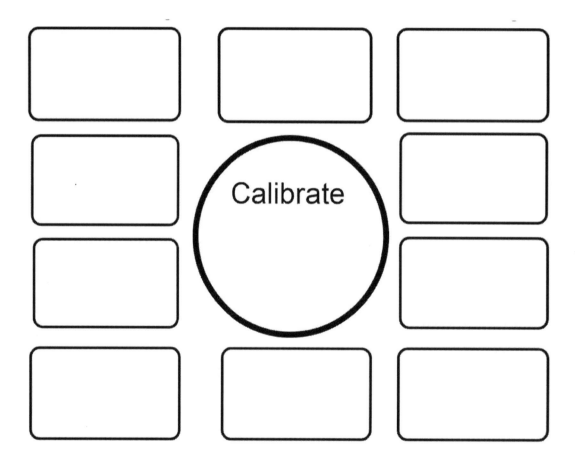

Get out ahead of it. Calibrate!

What is your point of attraction? Point in the direction of what you want.
Observe what your Inner Being knows. Tell it the way you want it.

_____

_____

_____

_____

_____

_____

_____

_____

_____

_____

_____

_____

_____

_____

_____

_____

_____

_____

_____

_____

_____

_____

Identify. Isolate. Calibrate.

Identify

Isolate

Calibrate

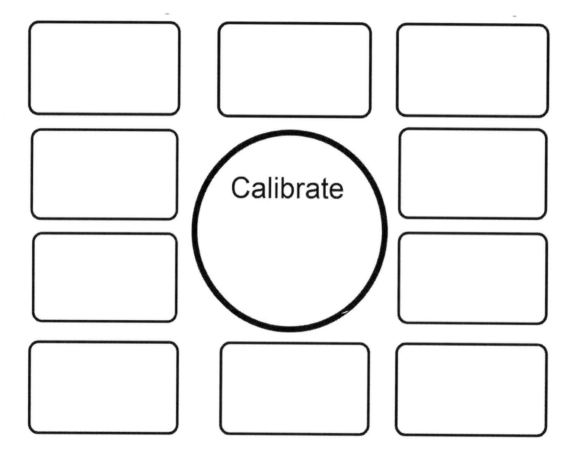

Get out ahead of it. Calibrate!

What is your point of attraction? Point in the direction of what you want.
Observe what your Inner Being knows. Tell it the way you want it.

_____
_____
_____
_____
_____
_____
_____
_____
_____
_____
_____
_____
_____
_____
_____
_____
_____
_____
_____
_____
_____
_____

Identify. Isolate. Calibrate.

Identify

Isolate

Calibrate

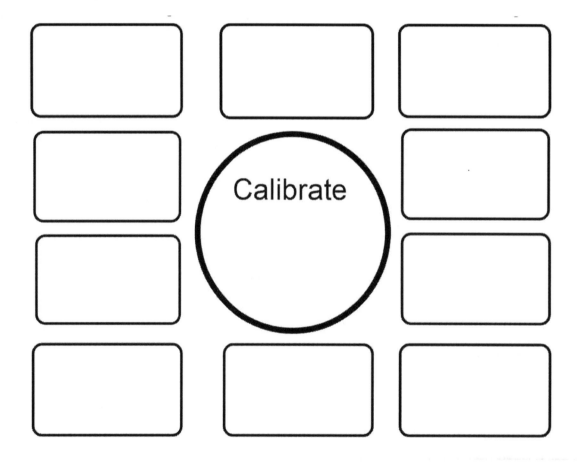

Get out ahead of it. Calibrate!

What is your point of attraction? Point in the direction of what you want.
Observe what your Inner Being knows. Tell it the way you want it.

_____

_____

_____

_____

_____

_____

_____

_____

_____

_____

_____

_____

_____

_____

_____

_____

_____

_____

_____

_____

_____

_____

Identify. Isolate. Calibrate.

Identify

Isolate

Calibrate

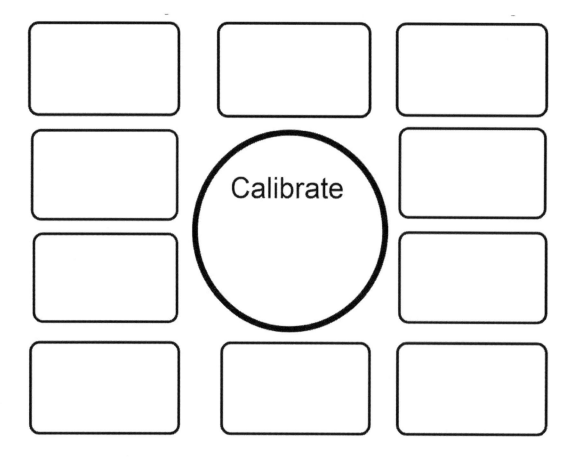

Get out ahead of it. Calibrate!

What is your point of attraction? Point in the direction of what you want.
Observe what your Inner Being knows. Tell it the way you want it.

_____

_____

_____

_____

_____

_____

_____

_____

_____

_____

_____

_____

_____

_____

_____

_____

_____

_____

_____

_____

_____

_____

_____

_____

Identify. Isolate. Calibrate.

Identify

Isolate

Calibrate

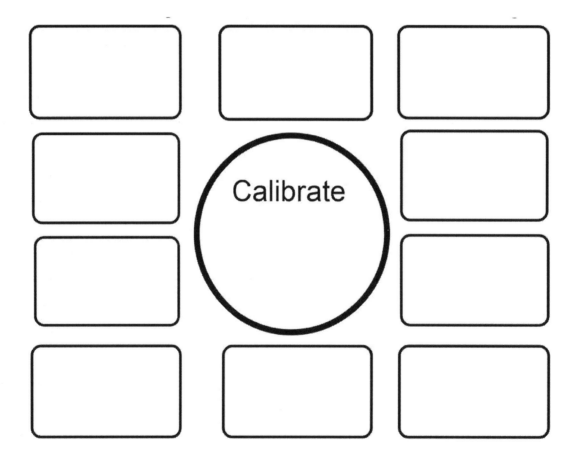

Get out ahead of it. Calibrate!

What is your point of attraction? Point in the direction of what you want.
Observe what your Inner Being knows. Tell it the way you want it.

_____

_____

_____

_____

_____

_____

_____

_____

_____

_____

_____

_____

_____

_____

_____

_____

_____

_____

_____

_____

_____

_____

_____

_____

_____

_____

Identify. Isolate. Calibrate.

Identify

Isolate

Calibrate

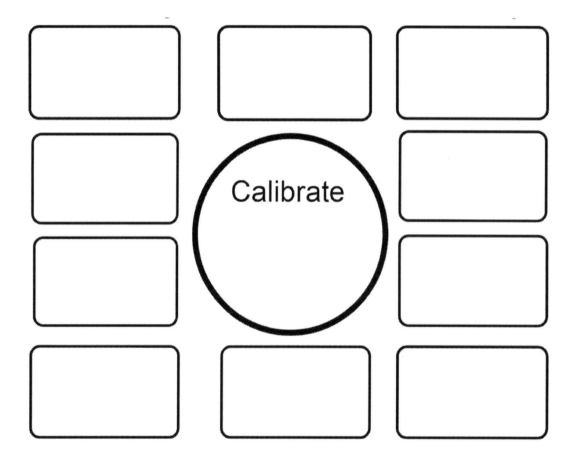

Get out ahead of it. Calibrate!

What is your point of attraction? Point in the direction of what you want.
Observe what your Inner Being knows. Tell it the way you want it.

_____

_____

_____

_____

_____

_____

_____

_____

_____

_____

_____

_____

_____

_____

_____

_____

_____

_____

_____

_____

_____

_____

_____

Identify. Isolate. Calibrate.

Identify

Isolate

Calibrate

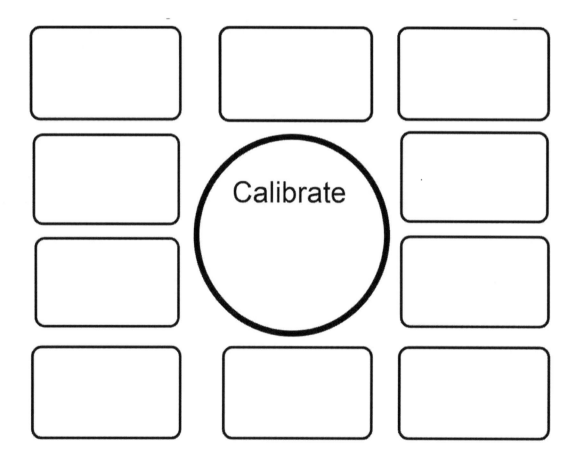

Get out ahead of it. Calibrate!

What is your point of attraction? Point in the direction of what you want.
Observe what your Inner Being knows. Tell it the way you want it.

_____

_____

_____

_____

_____

_____

_____

_____

_____

_____

_____

_____

_____

_____

_____

_____

_____

_____

_____

_____

_____

_____

_____

_____

Identify. Isolate. Calibrate.

Identify

Isolate

Calibrate

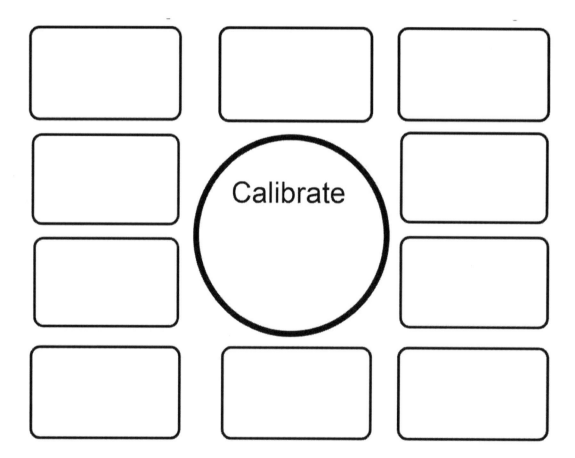

Calibrate

Get out ahead of it. Calibrate!

What is your point of attraction? Point in the direction of what you want. Observe what your Inner Being knows. Tell it the way you want it.

_____

_____

_____

_____

_____

_____

_____

_____

_____

_____

_____

_____

_____

_____

_____

_____

_____

_____

_____

_____

_____

_____

_____

Identify. Isolate. Calibrate.

Identify

Isolate

Calibrate

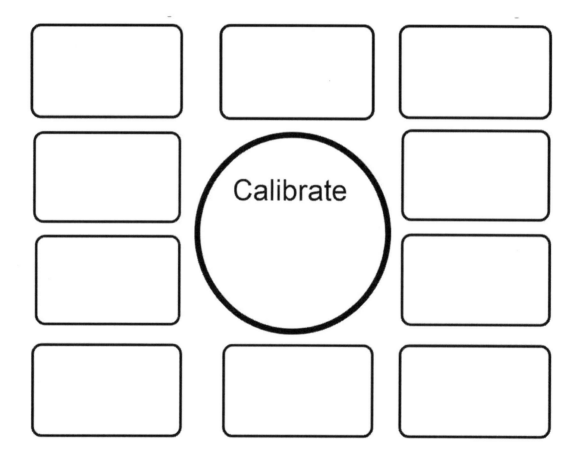

Calibrate

Get out ahead of it. Calibrate!

What is your point of attraction? Point in the direction of what you want.
Observe what your Inner Being knows. Tell it the way you want it.

_____

_____

_____

_____

_____

_____

_____

_____

_____

_____

_____

_____

_____

_____

_____

_____

_____

_____

_____

_____

_____

_____

Identify. Isolate. Calibrate.

Identify

Isolate

Calibrate

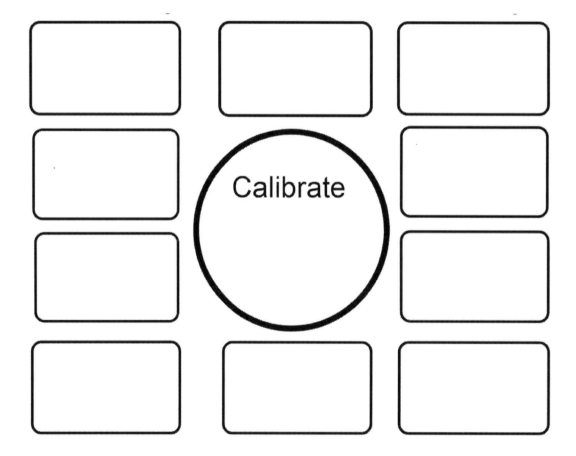

Get out ahead of it. Calibrate!

What is your point of attraction? Point in the direction of what you want.
Observe what your Inner Being knows. Tell it the way you want it.

_____

_____

_____

_____

_____

_____

_____

_____

_____

_____

_____

_____

_____

_____

_____

_____

_____

_____

_____

_____

_____

_____

_____

Identify. Isolate. Calibrate.

Identify

Isolate

Calibrate

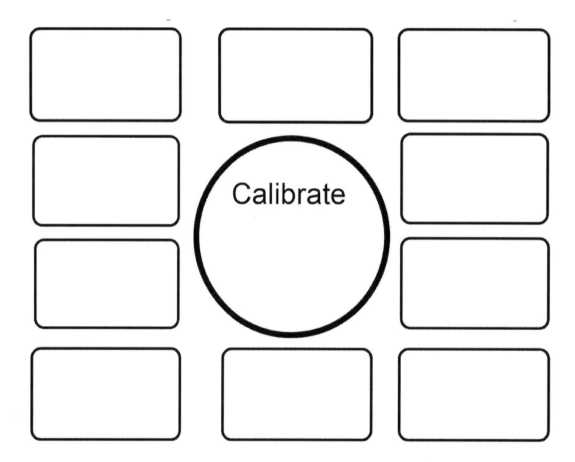

Get out ahead of it. Calibrate!

What is your point of attraction? Point in the direction of what you want.
Observe what your Inner Being knows. Tell it the way you want it.

_____

_____

_____

_____

_____

_____

_____

_____

_____

_____

_____

_____

_____

_____

_____

_____

_____

_____

_____

_____

_____

_____

_____

Identify. Isolate. Calibrate.

Identify

Isolate

Calibrate

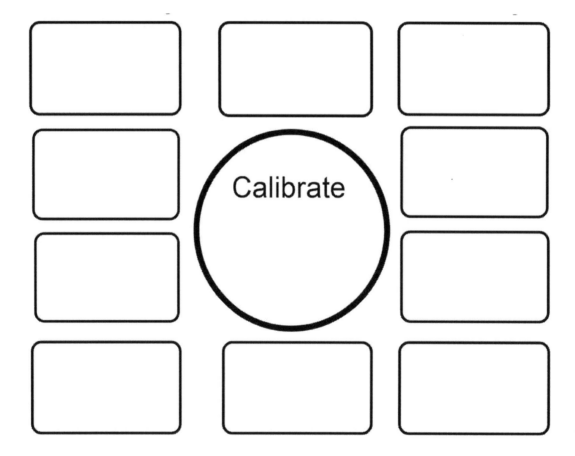

Get out ahead of it. Calibrate!

What is your point of attraction? Point in the direction of what you want.
Observe what your Inner Being knows. Tell it the way you want it.

_____

_____

_____

_____

_____

_____

_____

_____

_____

_____

_____

_____

_____

_____

_____

_____

_____

_____

_____

_____

_____

_____

_____

Identify. Isolate. Calibrate.

Identify

Isolate

Calibrate

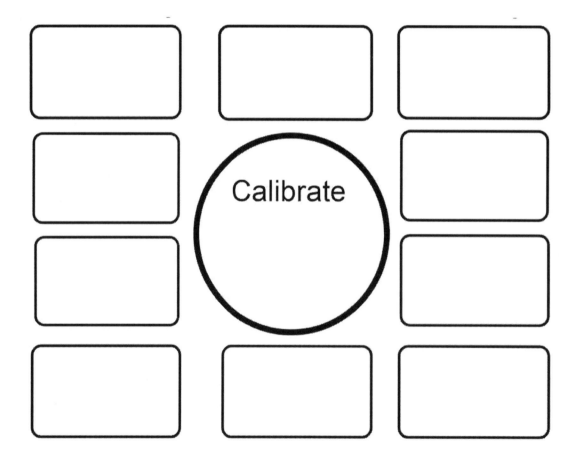

Get out ahead of it. Calibrate!

What is your point of attraction? Point in the direction of what you want.
Observe what your Inner Being knows. Tell it the way you want it.

_____

_____

_____

_____

_____

_____

_____

_____

_____

_____

_____

_____

_____

_____

_____

_____

_____

_____

_____

_____

_____

_____

_____

Identify. Isolate. Calibrate.

Identify

Isolate

Calibrate

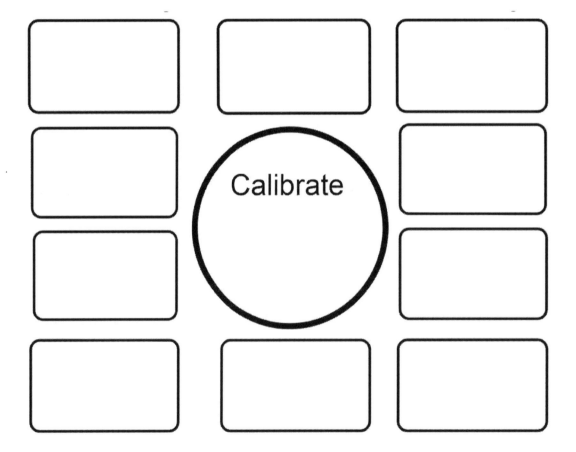

Get out ahead of it. Calibrate!

What is your point of attraction? Point in the direction of what you want.
Observe what your Inner Being knows. Tell it the way you want it.

_____

_____

_____

_____

_____

_____

_____

_____

_____

_____

_____

_____

_____

_____

_____

_____

_____

_____

_____

_____

_____

_____

_____

_____

Identify. Isolate. Calibrate.

Identify

Isolate

Calibrate

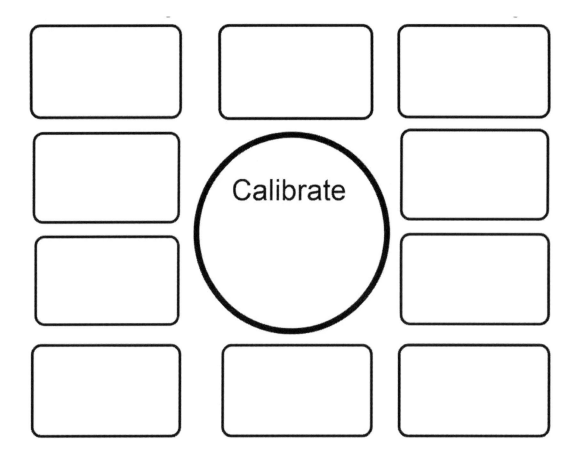

Calibrate

Get out ahead of it. Calibrate!

What is your point of attraction? Point in the direction of what you want.
Observe what your Inner Being knows. Tell it the way you want it.

_____

_____

_____

_____

_____

_____

_____

_____

_____

_____

_____

_____

_____

_____

_____

_____

_____

_____

_____

_____

_____

_____

_____

Identify. Isolate. Calibrate.

Identify

Isolate

Calibrate

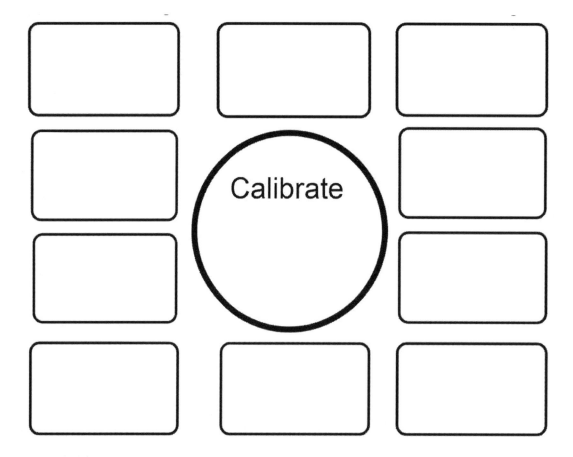

Get out ahead of it. Calibrate!

What is your point of attraction? Point in the direction of what you want.
Observe what your Inner Being knows. Tell it the way you want it.

_____

_____

_____

_____

_____

_____

_____

_____

_____

_____

_____

_____

_____

_____

_____

_____

_____

_____

_____

_____

_____

_____

Identify. Isolate. Calibrate.

Identify

Isolate

Calibrate

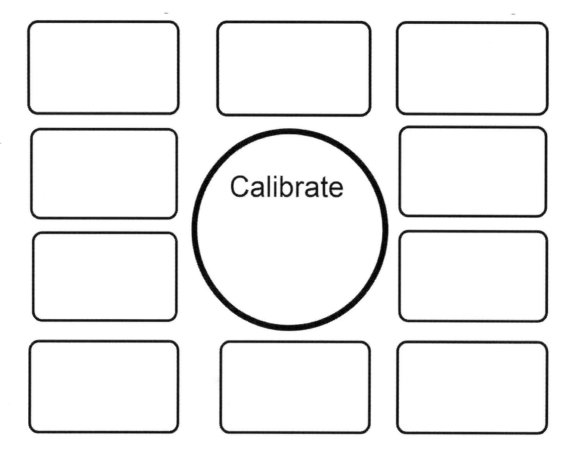

Get out ahead of it. Calibrate!

What is your point of attraction? Point in the direction of what you want.
Observe what your Inner Being knows. Tell it the way you want it.

_____

_____

_____

_____

_____

_____

_____

_____

_____

_____

_____

_____

_____

_____

_____

_____

_____

_____

_____

_____

_____

_____

_____

Identify. Isolate. Calibrate.

Identify

Isolate

Calibrate

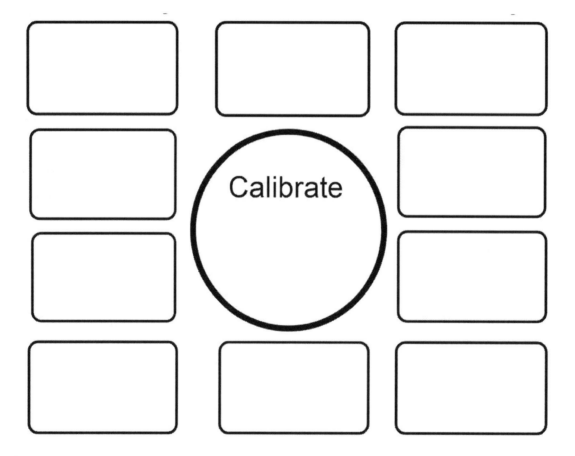

Get out ahead of it. Calibrate!

What is your point of attraction? Point in the direction of what you want.
Observe what your Inner Being knows. Tell it the way you want it.

_____

_____

_____

_____

_____

_____

_____

_____

_____

_____

_____

_____

_____

_____

_____

_____

_____

_____

_____

_____

_____

_____

_____

Identify. Isolate. Calibrate.

Identify

Isolate

Calibrate

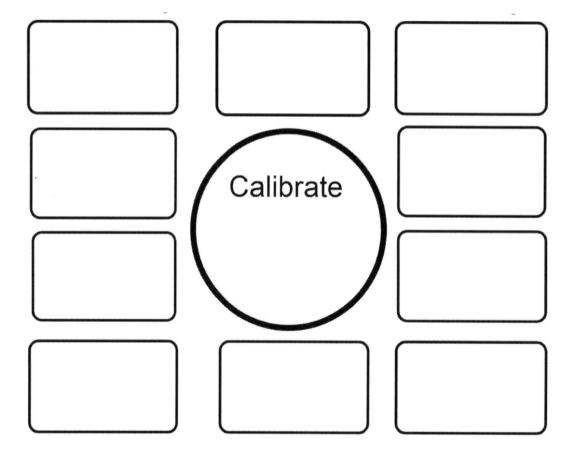

Get out ahead of it. Calibrate!

What is your point of attraction? Point in the direction of what you want.
Observe what your Inner Being knows. Tell it the way you want it.

Identify. Isolate. Calibrate.

Identify

Isolate

Calibrate

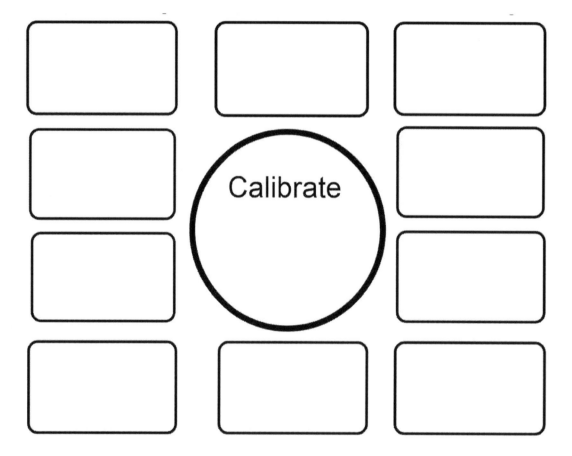

Calibrate

Get out ahead of it. Calibrate!

What is your point of attraction? Point in the direction of what you want.
Observe what your Inner Being knows. Tell it the way you want it.

_____

_____

_____

_____

_____

_____

_____

_____

_____

_____

_____

_____

_____

_____

_____

_____

_____

_____

_____

_____

_____

_____

_____

Identify. Isolate. Calibrate.

Identify

Isolate

Calibrate

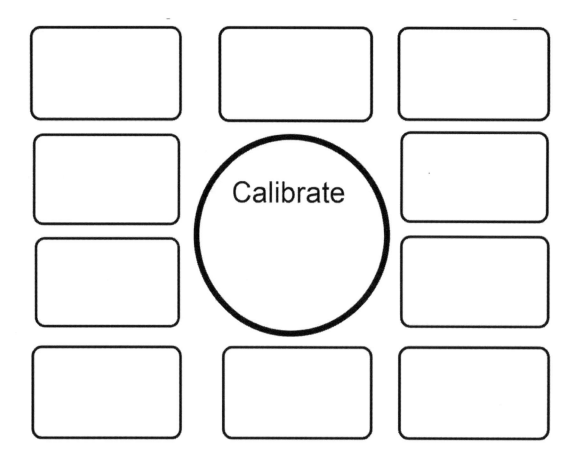

Get out ahead of it. Calibrate!

What is your point of attraction? Point in the direction of what you want.
Observe what your Inner Being knows. Tell it the way you want it.

_____

_____

_____

_____

_____

_____

_____

_____

_____

_____

_____

_____

_____

_____

_____

_____

_____

_____

_____

_____

_____

_____

_____

Identify. Isolate. Calibrate.

Identify

Isolate

Calibrate

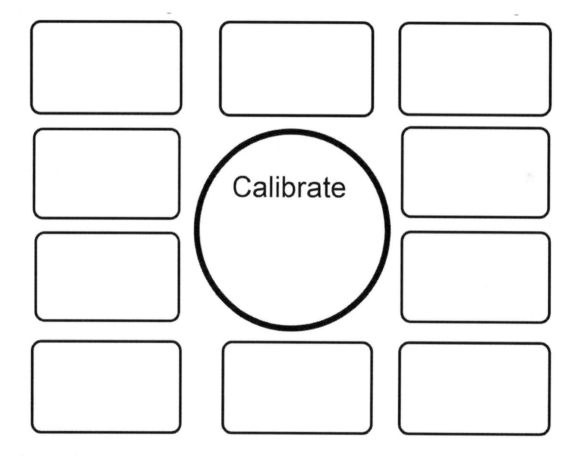

Get out ahead of it. Calibrate!

What is your point of attraction? Point in the direction of what you want.
Observe what your Inner Being knows. Tell it the way you want it.

_____

_____

_____

_____

_____

_____

_____

_____

_____

_____

_____

_____

_____

_____

_____

_____

_____

_____

_____

_____

_____

_____

_____

_____

Identify. Isolate. Calibrate.

Identify

Isolate

Calibrate

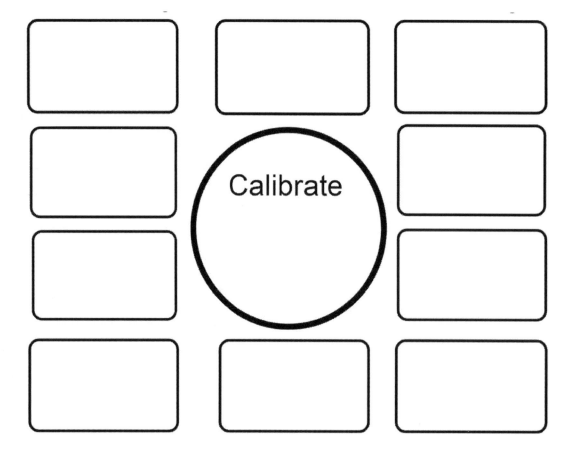

Get out ahead of it. Calibrate!

What is your point of attraction? Point in the direction of what you want.
Observe what your Inner Being knows. Tell it the way you want it.

_____

_____

_____

_____

_____

_____

_____

_____

_____

_____

_____

_____

_____

_____

_____

_____

_____

_____

_____

_____

Identify. Isolate. Calibrate.

Identify

Isolate

Calibrate

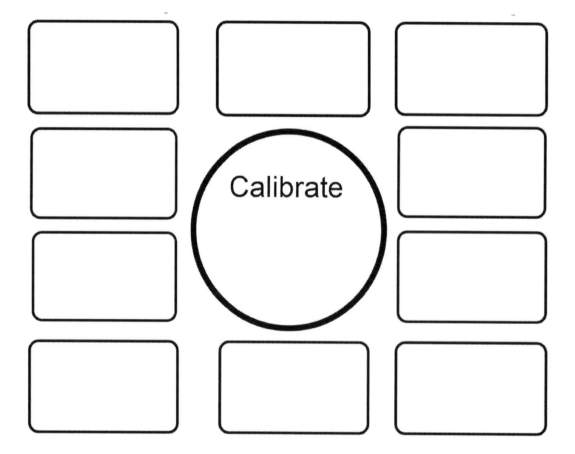

Get out ahead of it. Calibrate!

What is your point of attraction? Point in the direction of what you want.
Observe what your Inner Being knows. Tell it the way you want it.

_____
_____
_____
_____
_____
_____
_____
_____
_____
_____
_____
_____
_____
_____
_____
_____
_____
_____
_____
_____
_____
_____
_____

Identify. Isolate. Calibrate.

Identify

Isolate

Calibrate

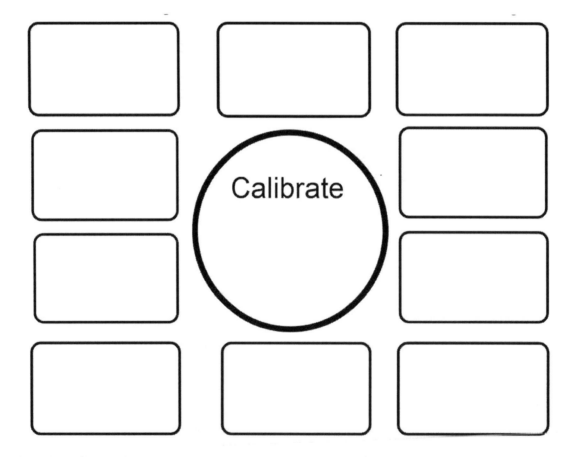

Get out ahead of it. Calibrate!

What is your point of attraction? Point in the direction of what you want.
Observe what your Inner Being knows. Tell it the way you want it.

_____

_____

_____

_____

_____

_____

_____

_____

_____

_____

_____

_____

_____

_____

_____

_____

_____

_____

_____

_____

_____

_____

Identify. Isolate. Calibrate.

Identify

Isolate

Calibrate

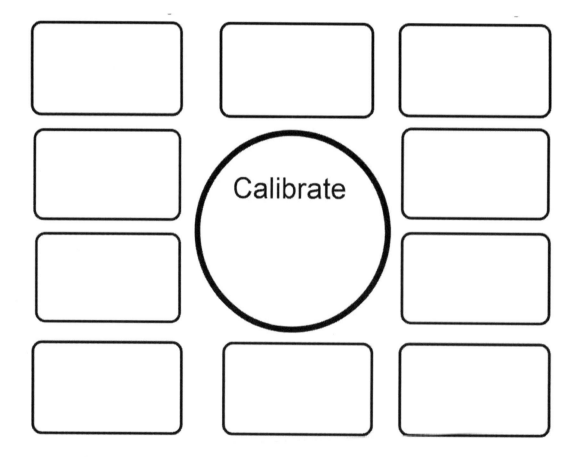

Get out ahead of it. Calibrate!

What is your point of attraction? Point in the direction of what you want.
Observe what your Inner Being knows. Tell it the way you want it.

_____

_____

_____

_____

_____

_____

_____

_____

_____

_____

_____

_____

_____

_____

_____

_____

_____

_____

_____

_____

_____

Identify. Isolate. Calibrate.

Identify

Isolate

Calibrate

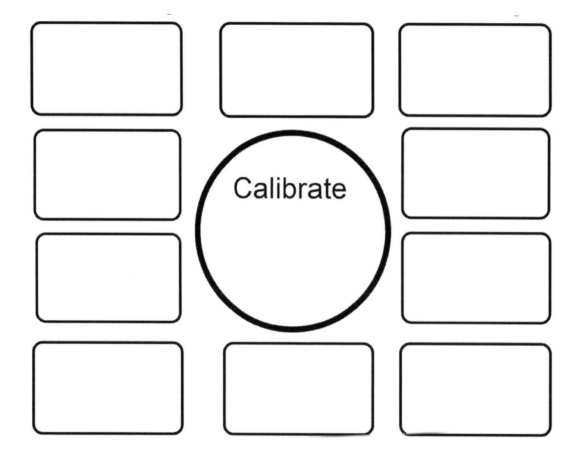

Get out ahead of it. Calibrate!

What is your point of attraction? Point in the direction of what you want.
Observe what your Inner Being knows. Tell it the way you want it.

_____
_____
_____
_____
_____
_____
_____
_____
_____
_____
_____
_____
_____
_____
_____
_____
_____
_____
_____
_____
_____

Identify. Isolate. Calibrate.

Identify

Isolate

Calibrate

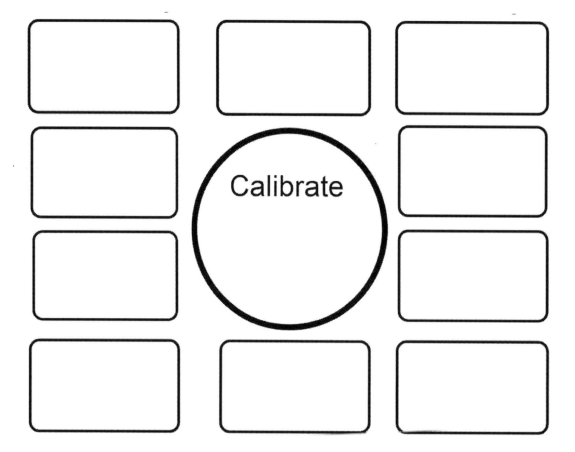

Calibrate

Get out ahead of it. Calibrate!

What is your point of attraction? Point in the direction of what you want.
Observe what your Inner Being knows. Tell it the way you want it.

_____

_____

_____

_____

_____

_____

_____

_____

_____

_____

_____

_____

_____

_____

_____

_____

_____

_____

_____

_____

_____

Identify. Isolate. Calibrate.

Identify

Isolate

Calibrate

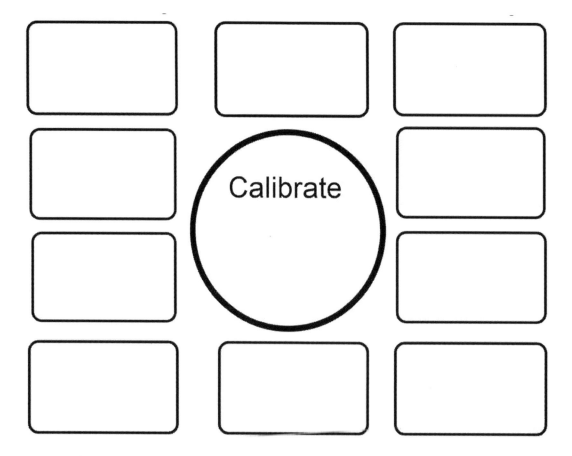

Calibrate

Get out ahead of it. Calibrate!

What is your point of attraction? Point in the direction of what you want.
Observe what your Inner Being knows. Tell it the way you want it.

_____

_____

_____

_____

_____

_____

_____

_____

_____

_____

_____

_____

_____

_____

_____

_____

_____

_____

_____

_____

_____

_____

_____

Identify. Isolate. Calibrate.

Identify

Isolate

Calibrate

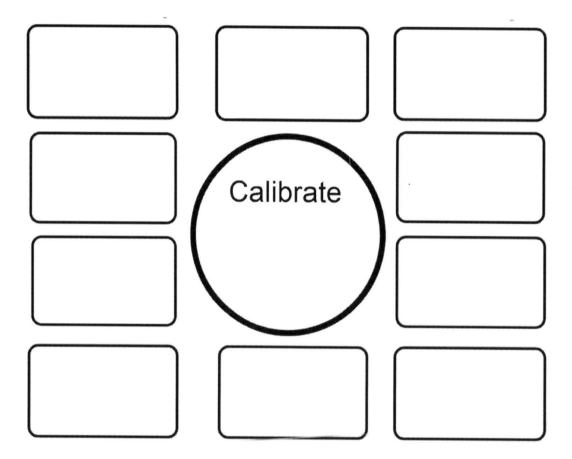

Calibrate

Get out ahead of it. Calibrate!

What is your point of attraction? Point in the direction of what you want.
Observe what your Inner Being knows. Tell it the way you want it.

_____

_____

_____

_____

_____

_____

_____

_____

_____

_____

_____

_____

_____

_____

_____

_____

_____

_____

_____

_____

_____

Identify. Isolate. Calibrate.

Identify

Isolate

Calibrate

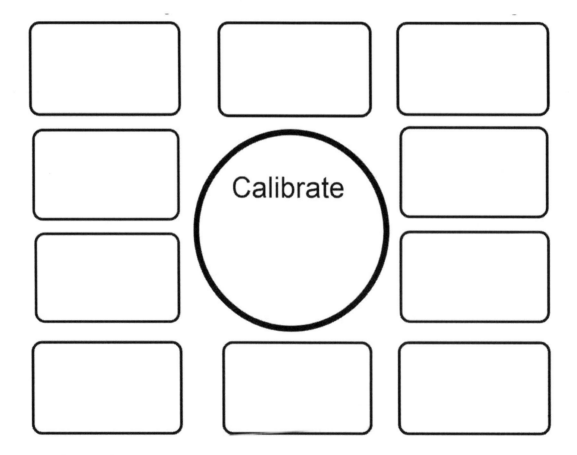

Get out ahead of it. Calibrate!

What is your point of attraction? Point in the direction of what you want.
Observe what your Inner Being knows. Tell it the way you want it.

_____

_____

_____

_____

_____

_____

_____

_____

_____

_____

_____

_____

_____

_____

_____

_____

_____

_____

_____

_____

_____

_____

_____

_____

Identify. Isolate. Calibrate.

Identify

Isolate

Calibrate

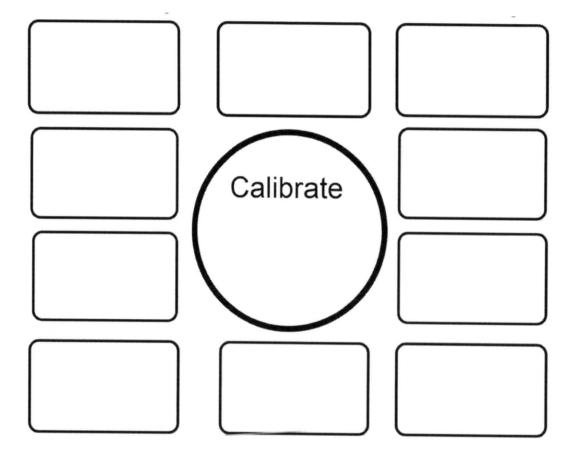

Get out ahead of it. Calibrate!

What is your point of attraction? Point in the direction of what you want.
Observe what your Inner Being knows. Tell it the way you want it.

_____

_____

_____

_____

_____

_____

_____

_____

_____

_____

_____

_____

_____

_____

_____

_____

_____

_____

_____

_____

_____

_____

_____

Identify. Isolate. Calibrate.

Identify

Isolate

Calibrate

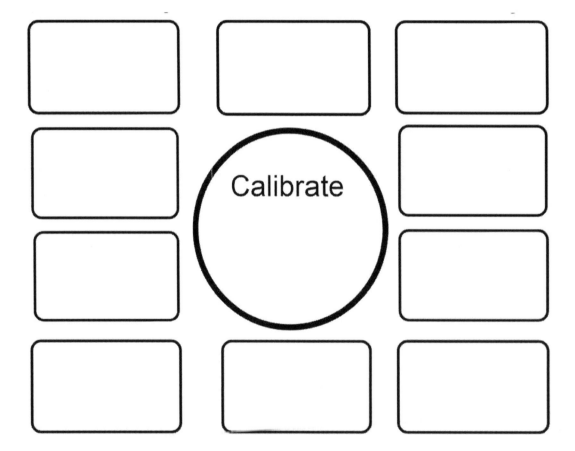

Get out ahead of it. Calibrate!

What is your point of attraction? Point in the direction of what you want.
Observe what your Inner Being knows. Tell it the way you want it.

_____

_____

_____

_____

_____

_____

_____

_____

_____

_____

_____

_____

_____

_____

_____

_____

_____

_____

_____

_____

_____

Identify. Isolate. Calibrate.

Identify

Isolate

Calibrate

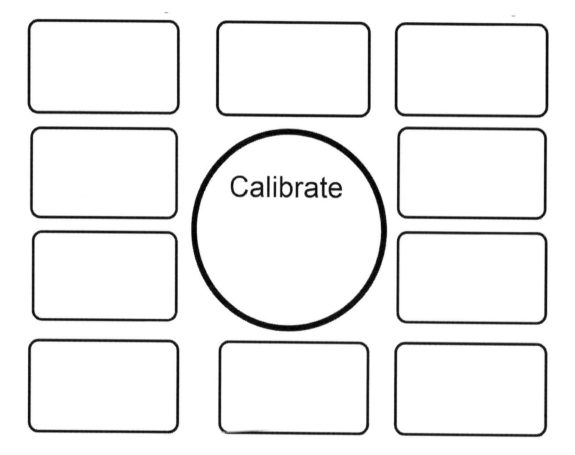

Get out ahead of it. Calibrate!

What is your point of attraction? Point in the direction of what you want.
Observe what your Inner Being knows. Tell it the way you want it.

_____

_____

_____

_____

_____

_____

_____

_____

_____

_____

_____

_____

_____

_____

_____

_____

_____

_____

_____

_____

_____

_____

_____

_____

All Things Law Of Attraction.com

(journals, workbooks, greeting cards, stickers, coffee mugs and more)

Law of Attraction Workbooks are influenced by
Abraham Hicks
https://www.abraham-hicks.com

Made in the USA
Coppell, TX
04 March 2022

74467071R00120